D1307183

# Biological Transport

# Biological Transport

## Halvor N. Christensen

*University of Michigan*
*Ann Arbor, Michigan*

W. A. Benjamin, Inc.    New York    1962

# BIOLOGICAL TRANSPORT

*Final manuscript was received May 7, 1962;
this volume was published November 15, 1962*

*The publisher wishes to acknowledge the
assistance of Oren Hunt, who did the
illustrations, and William Prokos, who
designed the dust jacket*

**W. A. Benjamin, Inc.**
**2465 Broadway, New York 25**

# Preface

What a strange field is transport! Here the investigator gathers information from kidney tubules, tumor cells, frog skins, gut sacs, and toad bladders. With such as these he observes behavior that violates the intuition of the enzymologist, morphologist, and chemist, and observes the behavior of molecules that may have proved inert in his every other test.

Biological transport is by no means a new subject, but it is one that has gained tremendously in interest from the various biological sciences in the last few years. The subject evolved from two rather discrete interests—that of permeability phenomena, extending back more than 60 years, and that of problems of secretion. The difficulties posed by the latter were found in the late 1930s to be associated with the former. With the closer approach to the interpretation of other cellular phenomena, the need to understand how substances and reactions are segregated and brought together in the cell and in the organism has become so pressing that many ingenious, indirect approaches to these questions have been discovered. Meanwhile, the search for the means to identify directly the structures producing transport has continued.

This presentation grew from a short series of lectures to an advanced biochemistry class, attended also by graduate students of pharmacology, physiology, microbiology, genetics, and other sciences. It should be interpreted more as a bibliographed syllabus for that instruction than as a review. Accordingly, the author has selected the illustrative material and examples that seemed most suitable and familiar to him. The result can hardly seem to have the ideal balance to all the scientific areas now interested in transport. Perhaps physiologists and pharmacologists would like to read more about the intricacies of ion transport, the physical and mathematical biologists more of the theoretical background, the cytologists more about the morphological substratum, and so on. Although all divergent needs cannot be met, I trust this summary will prove useful to both teaching and learning in various disciplines.

Thanks are due my present collaborators, Dr. Hitoshi Akedo and Dr. Dale L. Oxender; to numerous former collaborators for their participation in my attempt to understand transport phenomena; and to Dr. A. Baird Hastings and Dr. W. D. Stein for their helpful comments on the manuscript. I also want to thank authors who have kindly agreed to my use of figures and quotations from their writings.

H. N. CHRISTENSEN

*Ann Arbor, Michigan*
*May 1, 1962*

# Contents

# Biological Transport

# 1

~~~~~~~~~~~~~~~~~~~~~~~~

# *Scope of the problem*

## General

Many of the problems of life are transport problems. In the first place how did a sufficient variety and concentration of molecules get together to begin operations? Having solved this initial problem, how does the organism capture additional molecules to renew, energize, and replicate itself from an environment that may become very dilute? How does it avoid solutes present in the environment (perhaps produced by itself) at more than optimal levels?

Solutions to these problems obviously were reached. We cannot doubt that a great deal of concentrating of protoplasmic components takes place during life. If we permit, for example, a bacterial culture to autolyze, i.e., to hydrolyze its structure with its own enzymes, we shall find produced very strong solutions of some of the components that were originally drawn from a comparatively dilute solution in the culture medium. Obviously, concentration has occurred during assimilation, although we shall not find it profitable to use the term *transport* in a sense broad enough to include all events in assimilation. For our purposes, we shall limit transport to the mode by which a solute passes from one phase to another, appearing in the same state in both phases.

As the scope of transport is considered more closely, its importance to the unsolved problems of biology is seen to be very great. How does an organism carry out within itself so many chemical reactions that are inherently incompatible? No chemist would try

3

to perform simultaneously and in a single test tube the hydrogenation of a fat and the oxidation of acetic acid. These and dozens of other reactions must be kept apart. But, if barriers are placed between them, how can the product of one reaction be made to serve as the reactant for perhaps two others and still not be consumed by a third? How can each metabolic reaction be made to keep pace with others?

In the laboratory, the investigator establishes the course of a metabolic sequence by reproducing it one step at a time; first, he places the reactants and the specific enzyme for the first step in the test tube and then isolates the product; he presents the product to the second enzyme and makes the conditions favorable for the second reaction. Perhaps, under optimal circumstances, he may get two or three or more consecutive reactions to take place in a single solution in ordered sequence. But before long he must isolate an intermediate from the bulk phase and transfer it to another tube containing both the next enzyme and the coreactants for the following step of the desired sequence. In the cell, what machinery takes the place of the biochemist in shepherding a substance through an extended and complex sequence in the presence of perhaps hundreds of other related or unrelated sequences? Because many chemical reactions must be segregated, segregating and desegregating processes, that is, barriers and transport processes, are necessary.

One might suppose that a great deal of this necessary segregation of reactants and reactions could be accomplished by having different cells serve for different reactions. The nonbiologist would certainly suspect this from looking at the cellular structure of an organism and, particularly, at the division of higher animals into distinct organs. Here, of course, a degree of cellular specialization of chemical function is achieved because some cells synthesize, or modify or transport, particular metabolites much faster than others do. Urea synthesis or serum albumin synthesis and degradation come to mind. Such specialization of function requires that the plasma membranes around the cells be able to deliver a precursor from one cell into the intervening extracellular fluid, that the receptor cell be able to receive this precursor and release its product, and so on. In these cases, the transport problems have been met at or above, and not below, the cellular level. Differences in transport properties of cells underlie much cellular specialization.

Some of the most conspicuous cellular specializations are actu-

4

ally the production and release of control substances, the hormones, which serve to integrate various other metabolic steps. Others are the elaboration of the special environments represented by *secretions;* in this case groups of cells may spend most of their metabolic energy in transporting solutes into or out of such a secretion.

An overwhelming part of the problem of segregating biochemical reactions, however, is relegated to the *subcellular* level, and up to the present time has been only dimly perceived. Apparently all cells, even those of a complex organism, synthesize their own proteins and nucleic acids, generate their own power, and in general carry out many other metabolic steps independently. Steps that have been diminished or lost by one tissue or another during specialization of function do not necessarily seem to be the less compatible ones. In short life appears to have made very little use of the possible structural economy of the cell that seemingly could result from a high degree of specialization of cell function. Accordingly, the problem of segregation and transport undoubtedly is dealt with more at the subcellular level than at the plasma membrane or, for secretions, at a barrier formed by close-lying cells.

At the same time we may possibly exaggerate the extent of internal compartmentalization necessary to cellular function. As long as concentration gradients can be maintained by localized action, a wide range of conditions can be anticipated without having the cell be as compartmentalized as an onion. Even in cells containing very high proportions of organelles, 40 to 70 per cent of the volume may well be represented by a single-solution phase. In cells of certain types, electron microscopy shows reticulum lying layer-on-layer; but the observation of protoplasmic streaming and of small resistance to movement of objects argues against a universal, rigid organization of the cytoplasm of other cells. The similarity of the transport behavior of the adult human erythrocyte (or its ghost) to that of more complex cells indicates that our observations of the uptake and release of solutes by cells more often than not concern the behavior of the plasma membrane.

## Secretion

It is in the case of secretion that concentrative phenomena become most apparent. Aqueous solutions are produced that differ entirely from those from which their components come. A multicellular organism living in the sea may elaborate and maintain an extracellular fluid—an internal medium bathing its cells—having an entirely different composition from the salt or fresh water of the outside environment. In this case, barriers of cells lie between the internal and the external environment, principally at the gills, in the alimentary canal, and in the kidneys, and determine what solutes pass in each direction. Similarly, the land animal maintains the composition of its extracellular fluid by controlling exchanges across mucosal barriers.

Within the organism, secretions of still-different compositions are produced from the extracellular fluid. Typically, in this process a pool of the normal environment is first separated by a preliminary filtration or secretion; then a barrier of cells lying between this pool and the main portion of the extracellular fluid proceeds to enrich the secretion with certain solutes and to impoverish it with regard to others. In the specific case of the kidney, the blood passes through two successive capillary networks: In the first, ultrafiltration at the glomerulus (Figure 1) produces the primary flow; in the second, the blood is again brought into intimate contact with this flow, separated this time by a barrier of secretory cells; the cells transfer solutes from one aqueous phase to the other. Such a circulatory arrangement, passing through two successive capillary networks, is called a portal circulation.

Because the composition of secretions usually differs strikingly from that of the main bulk of the extracellular fluid, secretion was probably the first instance of transport to be recognized—over a century ago; the process still serves to convince the most critical observer that living cells may have highly developed potentialities for producing concentration gradients. Much more serious difficulties are encountered in proving that a given solute can be transported against concentration gradients into the cell itself.

We should note further that the enrichment of a secretion with a solute is often achieved indirectly, merely by withdrawing solvent from the stream of filtrate while preventing the solute in question from following the solvent. In the case of renal secretion, the extracting of water is also indirect, being produced by the transport of an important osmolite, especially the sodium ion, out of the ultrafiltrate; the water follows osmotically. This sequence is the one that causes many solutes, e.g., creatinine, to be far more concentrated in the urine than in the blood plasma.

6

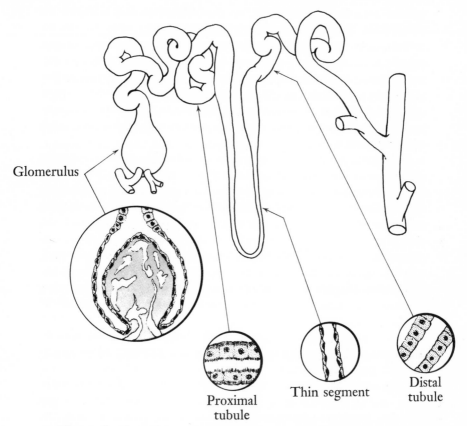

Glomerulus

Proximal
tubule

Thin segment

Distal
tubule

**Figure 1**   A nephron, the functional unit of the kidney. [*From Smith, H. W., The Physiology of the Kidney, Oxford, New York*, 1937; *with permission.*]

No adequate consideration of the role of secretion in the function of the multicellular organism, whether marine or terrestrial, can be provided to the student of transport within the space of the present volume. Everywhere one turns in the study of life functions, whether to respiration, digestion or excretion, or to special senses such as vision or hearing, he will find relevant aspects of secretion. The student who is not already informed of the great scope and interest of the subject should be referred to a textbook of general physiology.

7

## Transport into cells

Concern about the way in which cells gain their components from the environment goes far back in the history of biology. Tissue analyses were made over a century ago that were eventually understood to show potassium and magnesium to be the typical cations of the cell, whereas sodium and calcium ions are typically extracellular ions (cf. Manery, 1954). Until isotopes of the alkali metals became available, the magnitude of the problem of maintaining this biological situation was widely underestimated by assuming a static placement ("fossilization") of the cations in either one compartment or the other. In 1939 Cohn and Cohn showed that ionic $Na^{24}$ rapidly entered the erythrocytes in the intact dog, and in 1940 and 1941 Harris (see also Danowski, 1941) showed that a net exchange of sodium for potassium ion occurs when erythrocytes are cooled, or soon after they become depleted of glucose. Since these ions do steadily cross the membrane and since gradients of their concentrations are nevertheless maintained, a continuous transport activity must operate to maintain the asymmetric distribution of these two alkali metal ions.

In the paper introducing the term *pump* (without mechanistic implications) for an uphill-transport mechanism, Dean commented in the same year (1941): ". . . to assume that muscle fibers are normally impermeable to sodium and only excrete sodium when some gets in is not as simple as to assume that the fiber is permeable to sodium all the time and is continuously excreting it." (Perhaps we may also say that to assume that only secretory cells arranged as membranes are able to concentrate solutes is not as simple as to assume that all cells can do so.)

Packed cells contain such small amounts of characteristic extracellular solutes (sodium ion, chloride ion) that they obviously cannot admit the environmental solution to any great average depth. Instead, one finds present in the cell quantities of potassium and magnesium ions that presumably are nearly equivalent to the total negative charges represented by the anionic structure and machinery of the cell, plus a small amount of bicarbonate and even smaller quantities of other small anions. The relationship between the quantities of the osmolites and of water suggests an average osmotic pressure for a predominant portion of the cell interior close to that of the extracellular fluid. Such a relationship would hold if water could

8

move freely into and out of the cell. This is generally taken to be the case, although the view is seriously challenged by some investigators (cf. Robinson, 1954). Direct experimental measurements of the osmotic pressure of the cell interior are beset with great difficulties, especially in preventing spontaneous formation of osmolites. Means of avoiding these changes have been described, together with evidence that the osmotic pressure lies near that of the extracellular fluid (cf. Conway and McCormack, 1953; Brodsky *et al.*, 1953).

Obviously, we are not to think of the cell as filled with a homogeneous sap. The nuclear region may or may not be essentially continuous with the bulk of the cytoplasm, as far as the movement of small solute molecules is concerned, but the mitochondria and the endoplasmic reticulum undoubtedly present separate phases. For some cells as much as 60 per cent of the volume may be taken up by reticulum and other organelles. For certain other cells this proportion is small. The osmotic and transport behavior of the mitochondrion is an emerging subject, which we shall encounter briefly in Chapter 6. Electron-microscope studies have suggested to some cytologists (cf. Palade, 1956) that the cisternae formed by the endoplasmic reticulum may communicate with the exterior of the cell and, therefore, contain a fluid resembling the extracellular fluid (Figure 2). Such an arrangement, if it really exists, could increase the surface available to transport between the cellular and extracellular phases. As will be discussed on page 73, this interpretation has, however, only limited support and acceptance.

Although a free movement of water into and out of the interior of cells is widely believed to occur, at least some cells must present comparatively effective barriers to water movement; otherwise the urine and other secretions could not become hypo- or hypertonic to the extracellular fluid. This barrier action to water appears to be diminished by vasopressin, one of the polypeptide hormones of the posterior pituitary gland.

In the bacterial and plant world, the net osmotic movement of water may also be severely limited, apparently because of the presence of a rigid cell wall. Once this has been removed experimentally from bacterial cells, the resulting spheroplast or protoplast (Figure 3) becomes osmotically sensitive. The experiments of A. Fischer showed long ago (1897, 1900) that bacterial cells also are only selectively permeable and that they also possess a degree of osmotic sensitivity. It has been held in recent years that cells of coliform

9

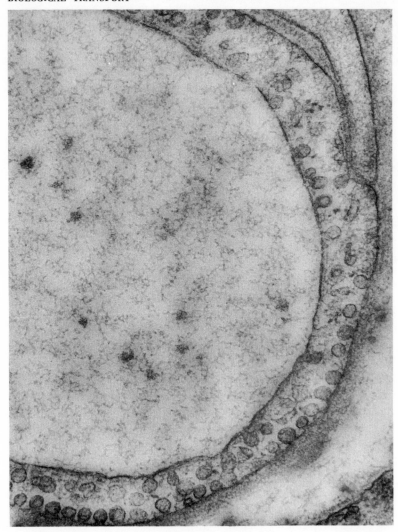

**Figure 2** Wall of a blood capillary in skeletal muscle of the rat. Small vesicles in the cytoplasm of the endothelial cells are shown; some of these are described as open to the cell surface and others as closed and probably deeper in the cytoplasm. Magnification ×73,000. [*From Palade, G. E.* (1961), *Circulation,* **24,** 371; *reproduced with permission.*]

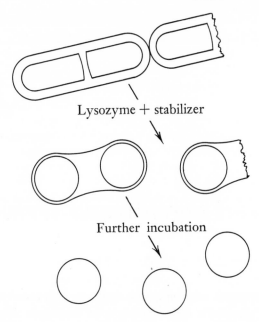

**Figure 3**  A sketch visualizing the formation of spherical protoplasts by lysozyme treatment of rod-shaped cells of *Bacillus megaterium*. [*From McQuillen, K.* (1956), *Symposium Soc. Gen. Microbiol.*, **6,** 129 (1956); *with permission.*]

organisms do not show selective impermeability to small solute molecules (cf. Roberts *et al.*, 1957), but this view meets much opposed evidence (cf. Mitchell and Moyle, 1956).

Accepting then the presence at or near the cell surface of a barrier that does not prevent the migration of water but which minimizes sodium-ion penetration and at which the sodium ion that does penetrate is extruded, we may test the proposition that it is this same barrier that controls the entrance of other solutes or that confines a phase into which solutes, in addition to potassium ion, are concentrated. The principal difficulty is to prove that the accumulated solute is really free and unmodified in the internal phase. For this reason, the reality of active transport into the cell cannot perhaps be placed on as firm a ground as can the concentrative nature of secretion from one extracellular phase to another. Some of the evidence on this question will be considered in Chapter 2.

# 2

## Concepts and terms

**Diffusion**

Although not a very effective form of migration when large distances are involved, diffusion becomes extremely effective for short distances and is undoubtedly the most important way in which metabolites move about in the cell. If one reaction produces a solute at point A and another consumes it at point B, the movement at a steady state can proceed almost as efficiently as if it were a directed flow. Furthermore, diffusion no doubt plays a part in all the other modes of transport.

The characteristics of diffusion are rather obvious. For convenience we shall consider molecules bearing no net charge, so that a contribution of an electromotive gradient to the total ("electrochemical") gradient may be ignored. The net rate of migration for such molecules depends on the concentration gradient, $S_1 - S_2$; the flux in a given direction through a membrane depends on the concentration (strictly speaking, the activity) in the phase of origin. (The term *flux*, we should emphasize, designates the *rate* of a one-way movement; therefore, we cannot correctly speak of *a rate of flux*.)

The flux ratio between two phases, as Ussing (1949) pointed out, therefore equals the ratio of their concentrations, $S_1/S_2$. At equilibrium for two similar aqueous phases, $S_1/S_2$ becomes 1. The linear relationship between concentration and flux will be found to hold with increasing concentration until levels are reached so extreme that one may suspect the nature of the membrane will have been changed. The diffusion rate depends further on the material traversed, represented in the diffusion equation by the diffusion constant $K_D$. This diffusion equation gives the velocity of migration for unit membrane area as:

$$|| \; V = K_D(S_1 - S_2)$$

The temperature coefficient of free diffusion in aqueous solution is low, so that the $Q_{10}$ is undoubtedly not above 1.5. On the other hand, Davson and Danielli (1943) have pointed out that diffusion across a thin lipid layer from one aqueous phase to another may be very slow and show a very high $Q_{10}$, so that a $Q_{10}$ of 2 or 3 or even higher cannot be taken to exclude diffusion as the rate-limiting step.

The diffusion constant $K_D$ measures the permeability of the membrane to the solute, that is, the ease with which the solute finds its way through the membrane. A membrane in the physicochemical sense is any boundary we choose to designate as separating two phases. In the biological sense, we usually mean to designate an anatomic structure. Notice that *permeability* is an appropriate term only within the subject of passive migration. To speak of the whole subject of transport as *the permeability problem* is to miss the mark badly, and to reflect an optimism of two or three decades ago that the whole matter of biological distribution could eventually be explained by passive permeation.

E. N. Harvey wrote (1943) about the cell barrier:

> Just as chemistry could not have developed without test tubes to hold reacting substances, so organisms could not have evolved without relatively impermeable membranes to surround the cell constituents. This barrier between the inside and the outside, the inner and external world of each living unit, has been and always must be considered one of the fundamental structures of a cell. No one can fail to be impressed with the great difference in properties of living and dead cells. The dead are completely permeable to diffusible substances, while the living retain one material and pass another. This difference, selective permeability, is so marked that it becomes the surest test to distinguish the living from the dead, holding where all other methods fail. It can truly be said of living cells, that by their membranes ye shall know them.

13

The plasma membrane restricts or almost entirely prevents the passive penetration of many solutes. For uncharged hydrophilic solutes, including water to the extent that its diffusion is restrained, the barrier action of the plasma membrane is believed to arise from a compact arrangement within it of the hydrocarbon chains of fatty acid esters, mainly phospholipids. This lipid layer is often pictured as lying between two protein layers in an organized, sandwich structure (cf. Davson and Danielli, 1943). For charged particles an additional barrier action may arise from a repulsion by polyelectrolyte

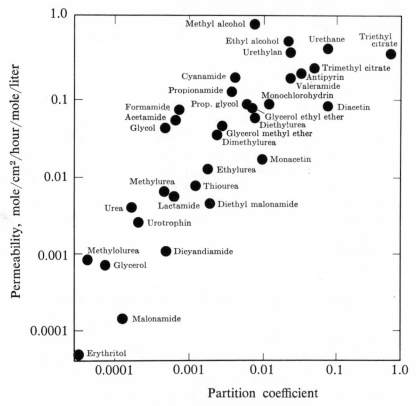

**Figure 4** Permeability of the cells of *Chara ceratophylla* to nonelectrolytes, plotted against olive oil–water partition coefficients. [*From Collander, R.* (1937), *Trans. Faraday Soc.,* **33,** 985; *with permission.*]

fields of the membrane, or even from single, well-placed, charged groups at channels that might otherwise serve for passage.

The evidence for a lipid barrier comes from a tendency of classes of small molecules to enter cells with rates more or less directly related to their degree of lipophilic nature, as revealed, for example, by their oil-water distribution coefficients (Overton, 1899, 1902). Classic results supporting Overton's hypothesis are shown in Figure 4. These observations were made by Collander (1937) on the plant cell, *Chara*.

The presence of a lipid barrier means that we cannot predict which molecules will pass the barrier—nor how rapidly they will pass—from their size and shape alone; we must also consider their polarity. As indicated a few paragraphs above, biologists hoped for many years that consideration of the factors of size, shape, charge, and polarity alone would serve to account for the full range of the movement of molecules. One should consult the writings of Osterhout (e.g., in 1933) for vigorous representations of this important point of view. We must continue to keep in mind the peculiarities of distribution that can be produced across a nonaqueous barrier.

## Mediation of transport

✓**Facilitated diffusion.** Many molecules, especially hydrophilic ones, show peculiarities in their migration through the plasma membrane, even though this may be downhill, i.e., in the direction of the concentration gradient. These peculiarities indicate that simple diffusion of the free migrating molecule cannot be the rate-limiting step. These are also generally the solutes that would not be expected to enter a lipid phase readily and which would require either an interruption of the lipid barrier or a modification of their physical properties to permit them to enter it.

For example, in 1925 Ege and associates noticed that the time for glucose to come to equilibrium across the human red blood cell from a 5.5 per cent solution of glucose increased from about 20 minutes to 3 or 4 hours when the temperature was lowered from 40 to 30°. Masing had already interpreted similar temperature effects with remarkable insight in 1914. But more significantly, the time to reach equilibrium at 30° fell to less than 1 minute when a 0.2 per cent solution of glucose in saline was used instead. Unfortunately, intermediate levels of glucose were not tested, so that the attention of Ege and his associates fell on the factor of the presence or absence of electrolytes in the suspending medium rather than on the factor of glucose concentration *per se.*

What one frequently observes is that, as the solute level is increased, the flux eventually ceases to increase but instead reaches a maximal value. This result implies that a reaction with a chemical structure or site present in a limited amount is necessary to transport,

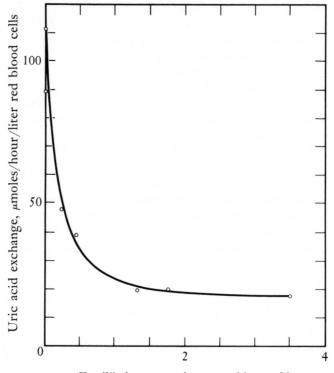

Equilibrium conc. hypoxanthine, m$M$

**Figure 5** Inhibitory action of hypoxanthine on labeled uric acid entry from 0.11 $M$ phosphate solution into red blood cells containing an equivalent concentration of unlabeled uric acid. Even high levels of hypoxanthine do not abolish one component of the entry. [*From Overgaard-Hansen, K., and Lassen, U. V.* (1959), *Nature,* **184,** 553; *with permission.*]

and that the supply of this structure comes to limit the transport rate at the higher concentrations. This structure or group is said to *mediate* the transport, and we thus have a *mediated transport.* If the transport is not able to proceed in an uphill direction, the mediation is a *passive* one, and we have what Danielli called *facilitated diffusion.*

Addition of a solute analog may serve better than an excess of the solute itself to demonstrate the limitation in the supply of the mediating structure. Figure 5 shows how inhibition by hypoxanthine served to demonstrate that most but not all of the migration of uric acid into the human red blood cell is mediated (Overgaard-Hansen and Lassen, 1959; cf. Lassen, 1961). [This result was obtained in 0.11 *M* phosphate medium. In Ringer solution no diffusion component is recognized (Lassen, 1961).]

If solutes diffuse through pores that are small enough, in relation to the size of the solute molecules, *restricted diffusion* may occur. In this phenomenon, the migration rate may cease to increase linearly with concentration, as more and more collisions occur unfavorable to passage through the pores (cf. Zierler, 1961). This phenomenon should be distinguishable from chemical mediation of transport by the following characteristics:

1. The analogs that most effectively inhibit the migration of a solute will themselves not pass as easily by restricted diffusion, whereas in mediated transport they will be transported more rapidly.

2. A flux in one direction would tend to be depressed by a flux in the other in restricted diffusion. We shall see below that the opposite effect has been observed for mediated transport.

3. One could hardly expect a significant difference in the passage of D and L isomers (e.g., D- and L-alanine) by restricted diffusion.

If no limits to the linear relationship between concentration and migration rates can be found, diffusion is still not proved to be the mode of transfer, since the capacity for mediation may be extremely high, either because the site is very abundant or because it functions very quickly. Even the very rapid entry of chloride into the red blood cell may be partially mediated (Tosteson, 1959).

*How mediation can occur.* To illustrate what is probably the simplest possible explanation, we shall choose a facilitated diffusion— the entry of glycerol into the human red blood cell. The erythrocytes of most other species admit glycerol only very slowly. As a

17

consequence, these cells may be kept for some time in isotonic glycerol, whereas the human cell is promptly lysed, for reasons that may be understood from Figure 6. An important spectrophotometric method for observation of high rates of solute uptake (Ørskov, 1935) depends on the swelling of the cells occasioned by solute entry or exit. The capacity of the human cell to admit glycerol is very high, so that one can show more easily that mediation occurs by adding an analog, 1,3-propanediol, than by adding excess glycerol. This analog has about 100 times as much affinity for the transport site as glycerol does. As an informative point, propanediol itself enters rapidly by other means, so that mediation for its migration is not easily detected. This rapid entry is ascribed to its more lipophilic nature, which presumably permits it to penetrate the lipid barrier easily.

The behavior that has so far been shown for glycerol transport could well arise simply from the presence of a fixed site on the red

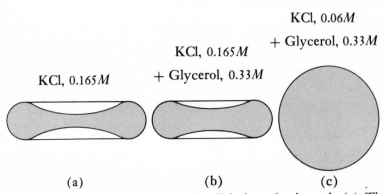

KCl, 0.165*M*

KCl, 0.165*M*
+ Glycerol, 0.33*M*

KCl, 0.06*M*
+ Glycerol, 0.33*M*

(a) (b) (c)

**Figure 6** The swelling of a red cell in isotonic glycerol: (a) The cell has been placed in 0.33 *M* glycerol; (b) hypothetical stage at which glycerol has reached a uniform distribution, but no water has yet entered the cell; (c) at this stage water has entered the cell until the internal salts are diluted nearly three times; at this point the cell is ready to burst, but there is still a difference in osmotic pressure, since more glycerol has penetrated with the water. Therefore, water entry will continue. [*From Davson, H., and Danielli, J. F., The Permeability of Natural Membranes, 2nd ed., Cambridge University Press, Cambridge, 1952, p. 24; with permission.*]

Membrane

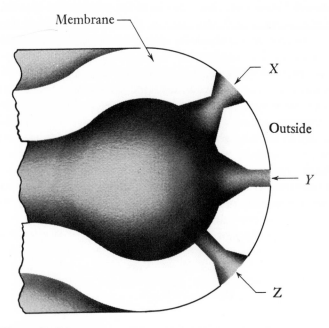

X

Outside

Y

Z

**Figure 7** Diagrams to represent simple transport sites: $X$, visualization of a chemical site located so that it can receive an appropriate solute molecule from either phase; once received, the solute molecule can be dissociated equally well into either phase; $Y$ and $Z$, sites constructed so they can receive solute molecules only from one side and pass them to the other, i.e., site $Y$ is supposed to be subject to mass-action effects only from side i, site $Z$ only from side o.

blood cell membrane, able to receive glycerol reversibly—equally well from inside or outside—thereby greatly facilitating the passage of glycerol. Figure 7 crudely illustrates such a fixed site. The inherent simplicity of such a fixed site may prove to be exceptional for biological transport systems. In fact, closer study of the glycerol system may yet reveal some of the complexities to be described later (page 21).

Very interesting evidence is available for the nature of the glycerol transport site. Cupric ion at $10^{-6}$ to $10^{-7}$ $M$ will block it; curiously, the effect is to protect red cells from osmotic lysis in glycerol solutions. From the fact that the cupric-ion inhibition can be relieved by free histidine, Stein (1958) argued that the binding site could not be a sulfhydryl group, as had been suggested. Instead he has reported in a preliminary paper (Stein, 1958) the detection of an N-terminal histidine whose reaction with phenylisothiocyanate can be specifically blocked by the presence of 1,3-propanediol. If this approach proves to have broad applicability, it should help very much in the identification of transport sites and the discovery of their function.

A series of fixed sites leading through the membrane and receiving the solute in turn, one from the other, with complete reversibility should yield the same behavior as a single fixed site. Figure 8 shows Danielli's visualization of a polar pore in a lipid barrier through which a solute could migrate, by hydrogen bonding, across the interval between pairs or sets of polar groups. Danielli (see the quotation, page 28) also considered the possibility that oscillations

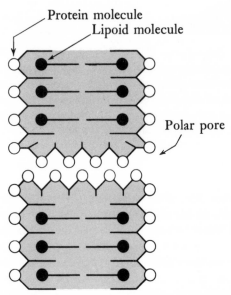

**Figure 8** Diagram of a polar pore in a lipid membrane, as visualized by Danielli. The pore consists of a succession of polar sites on polypeptide chains extending through the bimolecular layer of lipid. [*From Danielli, J. F.* (1954), *Proc. Symposium Colston Research Soc.,* **7,** 1; *with permission.*]

may occur in the structure of the protein components of the pore to assist in conveying molecules through the pore. But, if the polar groups lining the pore function only passively, the behavior should resemble that expected of a single fixed site.

We should not assume that facilitated diffusion necessarily has biological importance in every instance. The human red blood cell seems unlikely to need to receive glycerol at the unusual rate permitted by the glycerol transport site. Mediation may occur whenever a molecule finds appropriate spacings in the membrane structure, without reference to need. Höber (1902) wrote: "Utilizability or nonutilizability, usefulness or injuriousness, either in a recognizable or more obscure form, needs not be at all decisive for the question of uptake or non-uptake. . . ."

*The dimerizer theory.* Stein (1961a) has recently suggested that a pair of reactive sites receives two molecules of glycerol in such relative positions that they dimerize by hydrogen bonding to pass the lipid barrier in this lipophilic form. In this process, the usual hydrogen bonding of the hydroxyl groups of glycerol with water is temporarily interrupted, because hydrogen bonding to another glycerol molecule is favored. The dimer dissociates spontaneously on leaving the lipid phase. The kinetics of glycerol entry appear to indicate that two molecules of glycerol react, rather than only one. A similar proposal has been made for monosaccharide transport (Stein, 1961b). Under this interesting concept, one molecule of the solute serves as a carrier for another, and no interruption or polar channel in the lipid barrier is required.

**The phenomenon of flow driven by counterflow.** The diagram of Figure 7 presents a fixed transport site equally subject to mass-action effects from both sides. Suppose that we have a solute at an equilibrium, 1:1 distribution between the two phases. If we now add a high-affinity analog to one phase, we shall slow the flux of the original solute in both directions, but its distribution will not be changed.

This behavior should be contrasted with what is actually seen in certain instances. If a cell or tissue is permitted to come to a 1:1 equilibrium distribution with a given monosaccharide and a second competing monosaccharide is then added to the suspending solution, the first sugar may frequently be seen to move out of the cell to *create a concentration gradient* while the second sugar is entering the cell in the direction of its concentration gradient (Park *et al.,*

1956; Rosenberg and Wilbrandt, 1957). This behavior cannot result by simple diffusion under any reasonable assumptions (LeFevre and McGinnis, 1960), nor can it result with the single, fixed, symmetrically placed site of Figure 7. It could conceivably result if two entirely different fixed sites served, one for entry and one for exodus (Figure 7). Such an improbable arrangement could permit the added second sugar to lower by competition the entry of the first at site $Z$, without a corresponding effect on the exodus by site $Y$.

Most investigators feel it more likely that the entering solute causes the entry site to be reorientated to become, in effect, an exit site. This behavior implies that the transport site is *mobile*, or serves as a *carrier*. It would also permit the second sugar added to the external phase to compete with the original sugar and slow its entry, without having a corresponding effect on its exit; this effect would account for the original observation of Park *et al.*, in 1956. For sugar migration across the red blood cell membrane, this explanation appears to be sufficient.

In another case, however, namely, the uphill transport of amino acids into Ehrlich ascites tumor cells, separate estimates of the two opposed fluxes show that the effect is not adequately explained as a lowering of the parallel flux. Heinz had observed in 1954, without explanation, that a prior glycine accumulation in these tumor cells accelerated the subsequent uptake of labeled glycine. In 1958, Heinz and Walsh supplied further results showing that the glycine influx increased linearly with the magnitude of the cell glycine content (see Figure 9). Assuming that the influx had indeed been measured separately from the efflux, this result indicates that a *flux* can stimulate a *counterflux*, and not simply slow a parallel flux.

In the meantime Rosenberg and Wilbrandt (1957) had observed a corresponding outpouring of one sugar from erythrocytes when a second sugar was added, and coined the terms *flow driven by counterflow* and (Wilbrandt and Rosenberg, 1961) *counter-transport* for the phenomenon.

The results of Heinz and Walsh (1958), assuming that their separation of the fluxes was adequate, identified the behavior for certain amino acids as a mass-action acceleration of *exchange diffusion*, a phenomenon discussed by Ussing in 1949. If a chemical structure mediates transport across a membrane, it can obviously work in both directions, and much of the flux in one direction will

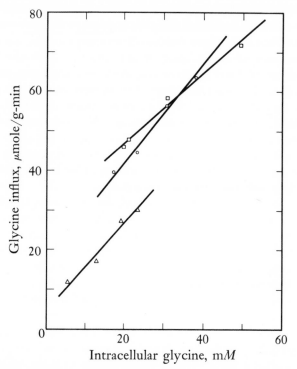

**Figure 9** Influx of glycine into Ehrlich cells as a function of the intracellular glycine concentration. (Three different experiments are illustrated.) [*From Heinz, E., and Walsh, P. O.* (1958), *J. Biol. Chem.,* **233,** 1490; *with permission.*]

be cancelled out by flux in another, so that net flux may be only a small fraction of the total flux. The influx of potassium ion into cells is ordinarily so high as to appear to require more energy than the total made available by cellular metabolism. It became necessary to assume that, for uphill transports, a considerable part of the total flux must also represent merely an exchange of the solute from the low-energy side of the barrier for other molecules from the high-energy side, without energy cost. Ussing warned that the isotopic method can lead to erroneous conclusions concerning the rate of active transport and its energy requirement, if part of the movement occurs by such an exchange of an external molecule for another of the same species already concentrated into the cell.

Figure 10 presents a model of carrier transport (Patlak, 1957), which we can use to explain the phenomenon of counter-transport as observed by Heinz and Walsh. The acceptor site, or "gate" ($G_1$), receives a solute molecule A at either face and, as a result, is reorientated so that when it dissociates it releases A to the other phase ($G_3$). If the gate can return freely to the first side to accept additional A molecules, the solute can eventually reach a steady-state distribution between the two phases. We shall assume for the moment that the system is unable to produce uphill transport. Obviously, the gate will then operate freely in both directions; in fact, at the steady state, equal fluxes will continue in both directions, and only *exchange diffusion* will be occurring.

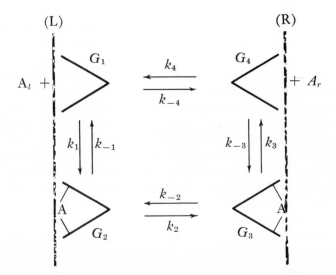

**Figure 10** A model for membrane transport. The gate $G_1$ receives the solute $A_l$ from the left. A reorganization is triggered orienting the gate toward the other phase ($G_3$) where the unchanged solute is released to the right. The gate can then be returned to its original orientation. If uphill transport is to be achieved, energy must be supplied to drive either $k_1$, $k_2$, $k_3$, or $k_4$. For example, energy may be supplied at $k_4$ to prepare the site so that the entry of $A_l$ from the left will trigger a relaxation to the condition $G_3$. [*From Patlak, C. (1957), Bull. Math. Biol.,* **19,** 209; *with permission.*]

The phenomenon of flow driving counterflow may then be explained as follows: Suppose we add to the right-hand phase at a high level A′, an analog of A. This solute will have a great tendency to migrate to the left through the system. As it does so, it may tend to orient more of the gates to the left than to the right. Accordingly, some degree of increase in the flow of A to the right (against the concentration gradient of A) will tend to accompany the large flow of A′ to the left.

On the other hand, if the gate is constantly and freely oscillating from the $G_4$ to the $G_1$ state, at least as readily as the solute-gate complex oscillates from the $G_2$ to the $G_3$ state, no influence may be produced by a flux on a counterflux; in this case, counter-transport can arise only from the inhibition of the parallel flux by an analog. This is the situation considered to hold for sugar migrations in the human red blood cell.

**Active transport.** Note that we have been caused to introduce *active* or uphill *transport* here in a section designed to consider instead the phenomenon of one net migration accelerating an opposed one. The striking aspect of this phenomenon is that it permits a transport, which does not in the usual biological context function uphill, to be made experimentally to function uphill. In the experiment of Park *et al.* (1956), it was shown that xylose moved out of the red cell to establish a concentration gradient after glucose had been added. The movement of one sugar on the addition of a second is uphill only to the observer, who differentiates between the two sugars; to the transport site, which does not distinguish between them, the total movement of sugar is, of course, in the direction of the over-all gradient.

In contrast to this behavior, several of the monosaccharides are normally transported uphill by the intestinal and renal tubular mucosa, without benefit of the driving force of a gradient of another sugar. We may consider, however, that the potential for uphill transport is built into transports that are mediated by a mobile site or carrier, even if they do not ordinarily function uphill. It is even possible that some uphill transports are driven naturally by the downhill movement of another solute, which may be the one primarily concentrated. This idea has been considered both for amino acids (Riggs *et al.*, 1958) and for sugars (Crane, 1960), with the gradient arising from the primary concentrative transport of an

25

alkali metal providing the energy. These proposals seek to explain the strong effects of alkali metal distribution on the transport of uncharged organic solutes.

In the case of amino acid uptake by cells, the presence of internal potassium ion and external sodium ion seems to be critical, and potassium ion migrates outward in exchange for sodium ion during amino acid uptake (Riggs *et al.*, 1958). For transmucosal absorption in the intestine, it is the presence of *sodium* ion that is critical (Csaky and Thale, 1960); this is also the case for amino acid transport into isolated nuclei (Allfrey *et al.*, 1961). For the uphill transport of galactose by kidney slices, both the sodium- and potassium-ion concentrations are critical (Kleinzeller and Kotyk, 1961).

We should examine once more the proposed phenomenon of flow driving a counterflow to see how it works in an active transport system. The cycle of Figure 10 can be caused to operate uphill by introducing energy at any of the four stages. For example, reaction $k_4$ may activate the gate so that it has a high affinity for A. The entrance of A into the gate may then trigger a reorganization that tends to orient the gate to the right side, with the result that A tends to be released on that side of the osmotic barrier. A large part of the energy introduced may then come to be represented by the higher concentration of A at the right. Accumulation will occur until the level at the right becomes high enough to compensate for the extra affinity of A for the gate at the left; if the membrane is free of leaks by which A can otherwise return from right to left, this steady state will show two equal and opposed fluxes through the system, and no net transport, only exchange diffusion, would be observed by separate tracer measurement of each flux. In some cases, evidence has been noted for the presence of separate leaks, either by diffusion or facilitated diffusion, in which case the transport system at the steady state will produce exchange diffusion plus enough uphill transport to compensate for the leakage. Notice that the exchange diffusion occurs without energy cost, i.e., without loss of the energy inherent in the presence of a molecule on the high-concentration side of the membrane.

In either case, the addition of a relatively large quantity of the solute to the right side of the membrane could again be expected to produce a counterflow, in accord with the results of Heinz and Walsh (1958), by accelerating the reorientation of the gate from right to left.

26

In carrier transport the actual movement of the carrier-solute complex is usually pictured as a diffusion, but other possibilities have been considered. Goldacre (1952) first suggested that the unfolding and folding of protein molecules could cyclically generate and destroy binding sites to produce transport. This effect was imagined to occur in the cytoplasm, as well as in the membrane, and to be the basis of protoplasmic streaming, to which transport was considered to be a side effect. The following separate sections of Goldacre's discussions (1952) are quoted to portray the nature of his proposal:

> When protein molecules are unfolded they have more surface area available for adsorption of other molecules than when they are folded up. The side-chains and other groups which are used to hold one part of the polypeptide chain to another part in a folded globular protein become free and turn toward the solution and can then adsorb other substances. . . .
>
> In the ameba the unfolded molecules in the cortical gel and plasma membrane should adsorb the material from the environment, and when they fold up in the tail, they desorb it. . . .
>
> Protein folding and unfolding appear therefore to be required for something much more fundamental [than osmotic work and cytoplasmic streaming] in the cell. This probably involves enzyme reactions which are assisted by this rhythmic change in the form of the molecule. The products of the reaction would be squeezed off the surface of the molecule when it folded up, but while adsorbed it would be kept out of the back reaction. . . .
>
> In this way ATP, which works the folding-unfolding cycle, could be harnessed to drive any other reaction which involves the folding-unfolding cycle (coupling) . . . A muscle cell for example is not something apart but an ordinary cell in which the already contractile protein chains are aligned so that the contraction of the cell all at once becomes a conspicuous feature. The same contractile chains can do other things as well, e.g., osmotic work and secretion.

The potentialities for transport inherent in changes in the tertiary structure of protein molecules are now widely appreciated, although today we may be inclined to think that denaturation might destroy or translocate active sites rather than unmask them. In general, models in which the solute molecule is directly propelled through the osmotic barrier by an event stimulated by its entry into the binding site, and in which the site becomes externally available again after reactivation, appear to have two advantages: first, an ATP-generating system outside the barrier is not needed; furthermore, a secondary barrier is not needed to retain the carrier-solute complex until it crosses the osmotic barrier.

As we have already seen, Danielli (1954) suggested that a pore formed with polar elements of protein structure might conduct solutes through the membrane (see Figure 8). This arrangement would produce only a simple facilitated diffusion if each stage of the migration were fully reversible. But, if the transfer of a solute occasioned a structural change at any stage in this sequence, interfering with its reversibility, the phenomenon of flow driving counterflow could be produced. Indeed, Danielli (1954) and Stein and Danielli (1956) pointed out that uphill transport could arise utilizing the energy that might be made available from structural changes triggered by the passage of the solute molecule. The following extended passage represents an attempted synthesis of evidence and ideas offered by Danielli in 1954:

> If the data and considerations presented above are brought together to present a general picture of the plasma membrane we must take into consideration:
>
> (a) the "sandwich" structure of the membrane;
>
> (b) its approximation to a homogeneous lipoid layer;
>
> (c) that abnormal permeabilities may be explained if in some areas a polar structure extends right through the membrane;
>
> (d) that enzymes are present at the sites of transfer, as shown by cytochemical methods;
>
> (e) that poisons for these same enzymes selectively block transfer;
>
> (f) some enzymes are known to provide the mechanism whereby chemical energy may be used to activate a contractile protein mechanism;
>
> (g) to facilitate permeation of polar molecules, hydrogen bonds between the molecules and water must be broken; this can be done by supplying protons or alternative hydrogen-bond-forming groups;
>
> (h) hydrolytic enzymes, such as phosphatases and esterases, probably work by providing a stereochemically specific hydrogen-bonding proton-conducting surface (just as the non-specific hydrolytic catalysis characteristic of ionic resins and ionic colloidal micelles is probably due to their non-specific proton-conducting surfaces);
>
> (i) so far as can be seen, the specificity for certain molecules, both of enzymes and of transfer processes, must depend upon the same organization of groups in space, both with respect to their nature and their critical spacing and orientation.

All the above points are provided for if we adopt the hypothesis that facilitated diffusion involves movement through a pore or slit composed of the polar groups of protein lamellae . . . The junction between two protein lamellae will not be a simple aqueous pore: it will be a region composed of polar groups and including a good deal of water, as is the case with protein crystals, and extensive hydrogen bonding between the protein chains will give it a unique character. The properties of this polar pore will include:

(i) ready permeability to small hydrogen-bond-forming molecules such as water and formamide.

(ii) if the protein component is positively charged, e.g. if it were haemoglobin, it would be selectively permeable to small anions, and thus provide the facilitated diffusion mechanism in red cells suggested by Davson. If negatively charged it would be selectively permeable to small cations.

(iii) to larger polar molecules the pore would be permeable only if the structure and configuration of the molecule conformed to the structure of the pore.

(iv) passage through such a pore need not occur by movement of the penetrating molecule only. We can envisage the protein components of such pores oscillating between different configurations. Examples of such oscillations are found in reversibly denatured proteins. Such oscillations may assist in conveying molecules through the membrane.

(v) a pore of this nature offers a basis for working out possible modes of action of hormones, such as insulin and "growth" hormone, which are concerned in transfer processes.

(vi) a pore of this character provides a mechanism which will permit proteins to pass through plasma membranes. The possibility of such passage would depend upon the specific configurations of the proteins of the pore and of the permeating protein, and a mechanism of this type may account for selective permeability to proteins of the type reported by Brambell and Hemmings for the passage of antibodies through the intestinal wall, etc.

(vii) pores of this character would not only exert the selectivity characteristic of facilitated diffusion, but would also be susceptible to the action of enzyme poisons. . . .

In short, a pore structure of this type appears to provide an excellent working hypothesis for study in connection with facilitated diffusion. The components of the pore need not be entirely restricted to protein, but might include nucleic acids, polysaccharides, etc. This conception has the additional advantage that by simple extension the mechanism of facilitated diffusion becomes a mechanism of active transport. Where movement of the penetrating species is determined by the kinetic energy of alternative structures under the influence of thermal agitation, the

29

process is facilitated diffusion. But if the movement is determined by a contraction-expansion, or oscillation, impressed upon a protein by the energy released by the enzymic action of that protein, then we have active transfer. Thus Goldacre's (1952) concept of the importance of contractile proteins in active transport becomes logically connected with the mechanism deduced for facilitated diffusion.

Other writers have suggested instead that continuous, spontaneous mechanical movements of the membrane might cause binding groups to function to produce uphill transport. Such a behavior, although presumably wasteful in terms of energy, could probably also permit flow to drive counterflow.

The lesson taught by the close relationship between the mediated transport that is not uphill, on the one hand, and the mediated transport that functions uphill, on the other, is that we cannot afford to limit our attention to active transports. Amino acid transport is uphill in the reticulocyte (Riggs et al., 1952), but apparently it ceases to work uphill after the reticulum is lost (Riggs et al., 1952; Winter, 1962). One should also remember that a transport capable of generating a gradient does not wait until the 1:1 distribution ratio is passed to begin to operate. The refined criterion of Ussing (1949) for active transport takes account of this difficulty. This criterion says that, when the flux ratio exceeds the ratio of electrochemical gradients, an active transport must be occurring.

Occasionally the term *active transport* is applied incorrectly when only a dependence on a metabolic, energy-yielding process has been shown. This cannot be considered a reliable indication that the transport is uphill. Perhaps the most convincing lines of evidence that the uptake by cells is active are two: first, the gradients in some cases may exceed the plausible limits for binding agents. For example, the muscles of some marine crustaceans contain upward of a 1-$M$ level of amino acids collectively, including taurine. The Ehrlich tumor cell may attain gradients of 60 to 160 m$M$ for a single amino acid. Few possible binding sites are present at such levels. Second, water movements can often be demonstrated in approximately direct relationship to solute uptake. This relationship was shown for glycine uptake by the Ehrlich cell (Christensen, 1955) as illustrated in Figure 11, and for lactose uptake by E. coli spheroplasts in Figure 12 (Sistrom, 1958).

A more elaborate demonstration that the activity of the Ehrlich

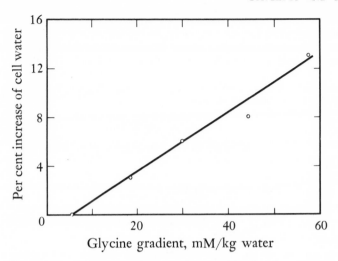

**Figure 11** Water uptake associated with the development of a glycine gradient by Ehrlich ascites tumor cells. The line corresponds to the predicted isoosmotic uptake of water assuming 70 per cent of the accumulated glycine to be osmotically active, and assuming that no other solutes migrate. [*From Christensen, H. N. (1955), in W. D. McElroy and B. Glass (eds.), Amino Acid Metabolism, Johns Hopkins Press, Baltimore, p. 82; with permission.*]

cell for amino acids is really concentrative was made by Oxender and Christensen (1959). On filtering a cell suspension, these cells were collected on the filter in the form of a membrane-like layer a few cells thick. When this membrane was exposed to a gradient of pyridoxal, alanine, or potassium ion, glycine—previously distributed uniformly between the two phases separated by the membrane—moved across the cell barrier to form a small gradient opposite in sign to the imposed gradients. These three agents are able to stimulate or inhibit the uptake of glycine by the Ehrlich cell when placed in its environment. Presumably, transport across the cells occurred in the present instance because this stimulation or inhibition was applied more strongly on one side of the cell than on the other. In this case substantial volumes of extracellular fluid were available for critical examination. The supposition is that the gradients of the other solutes produced an asymmetry in the concentrative activity from the two sides of the cells, so that part of the concen-

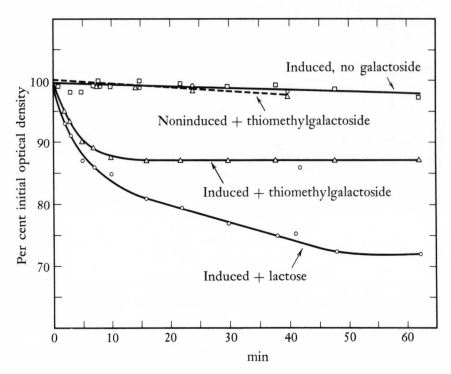

**Figure 12** The effect of adding β-galactosides (0.01 *M*) on the optical density of osmotically sensitive *E. coli* spheroplasts. The optical density changes measure the degree of swelling. [*From Sistrom, W. R.* (1958), *Biochim. et Biophys. Acta*, **29,** 584; *with permission.*]

trative activity of the cell could be recorded in an extracellular fluid.

For solutes with a net charge, such as potassium or sodium ions, particular care must be taken to verify that net migration actually occurs against the *electrochemical gradient*, i.e., that a potential gradient across the membrane does not account for the development of a chemical gradient. Biological phases usually contain non-diffusible, macromolecular anions, which characteristically produce Gibbs-Donnan effects, including potential differences and gradients of ion concentrations. Since cells ordinarily contain substantially higher levels of such anions than the surrounding solutions do, the alkali metal cations tend to enter the cells against chemical gradients. Were this tendency not opposed by active extrusion of sodium ion, this uptake would continue to provoke water uptake and swelling until the cells would be destroyed. The diagrammatic representation of Figure 13 will serve to remind one of the origin of this osmotic pressure difference. For this reason, destructive osmotic swelling of cells tends to result whenever alkali metal transport is inhibited (cf., for example, Wilson, 1954). As noted earlier in this discussion, only a high degree of cation impermeability was at one time believed to protect cells from destruction by the osmotic forces arising from the tendency of ions and water to be taken up. The following words by Harris (1941) show how this concept changed:

> It is believed that a cation impermeability of the erythrocytes prevents their rupture by the osmotic force of the Gibbs-Donnan equilibrium. However, the same result can be achieved, although in a different way, if the metabolic activity of the cells controls the distribution of cations even though the membrane be considered permeable to sodium and potassium. Indeed, because of this activity and the apparently very slow rate of permeation of cations, as compared to anions, the membrane may be said to be functionally impermeable to the positive ions, at least as regards such functions as the transport of $CO_2$. Thus, the calculations of Van Slyke et al. (1923) and more recently of Rapoport and Guest (1939), showing that the anions of blood tend to distribute themselves according to the Donnan equilibrium (assuming cation impermeability), lose none of their significance.

In the case of muscle fiber, the potential differences involved may possibly be sufficient to account for the cellular potassium content so that sodium-ion extrusion would account for alkali metal distribution without invoking an active potassium-ion uptake. A direct linkage between sodium- and potassium-ion transfer is nevertheless suspected. For the human red blood cell, the asymmetry of the chloride distribution (the concentration being about 70 per cent as great in the cell water as in the plasma water at pH 7.4) provides an estimate of the potential difference across the membrane and shows that its value cannot be great enough to account for the 30:1 distribution ratio for the potassium ion; hence, an active up-

33

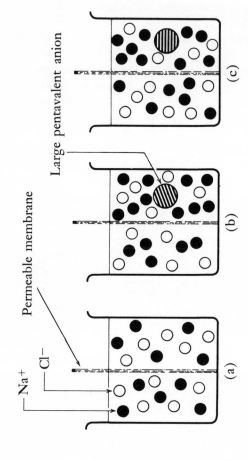

Na+

Permeable membrane

Cl−

Large pentavalent anion

(a)                (b)                (c)

**Figure 13** Diagrammatic representation of the Gibbs-Donnan equilibrium. It is assumed that (a), NaCl is initially distributed evenly between two aqueous compartments, the separating membrane being easily permeated by Na+ and Cl−. This equilibrium is represented diagrammatically by the presence of five sodium ions and five chloride ions in each compartment; (b), a quantity of sodium proteinate is then added to the right-hand compartment. The large polyvalent anion is unable to pass through the membrane. Na+ will now tend to pass to the right to equalize the two Na+ levels, but at the same time Cl− must also pass to the left, thereby creating a Cl− gradient. At equilibrium, (c), $(Na^+)_1(Cl^-)_1 = (Na^+)_2(Cl^-)_2$ as shown in the sketch. Notice that the right-hand compartment has two extra particles: the nondiffusible anion and one extra diffusible ion; i.e., $(4 + 9) > (6 + 6)$. Hence the presence of the nondiffusible anion has produced a distinct osmotic pressure difference.

34

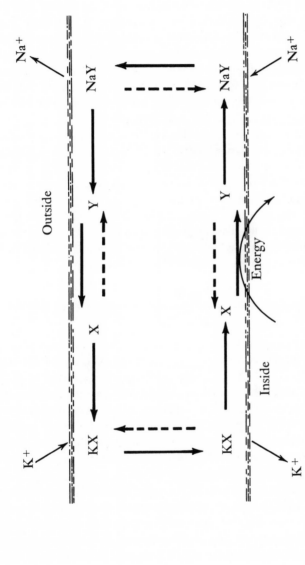

**Figure 14** Shaw's hypothesis of a carrier for potassium ion, converted to a carrier for sodium ion by linkage to an energy-yielding reaction. [*From Glynn, I. M.* (1957), *Progr. Biophys. Biophys. Chem.,* **8**, 292; *with permission.*]

take of this cation, as well as an active extrusion of sodium ion, appear inescapable for these cells. Evidence has accumulated that sodium-ion extrusion and potassium-ion uptake are probably linked into a single process. Sodium-ion efflux in many tissues has been found to be sharply diminished in the absence of potassium ion in the external medium. Consideration is often given to a carrier with an affinity for potassium ion which may be converted to another carrier that binds sodium ion (Shaw, 1954). Figure 14 shows Shaw's model as redrawn by Glynn (1957a). We shall see below that both ions must be present for the enzymatic catalysis of an ATP cleavage believed to provide energy for their transport.

A potential gradient, rather than producing a chemical gradient, may arise from the active transport of ions across a membrane. Ussing and Zerahn (1951) showed that sodium-ion transport across frog skin continues unchecked when the potential difference across the skin is cancelled out by experimentally opposing an equal potential. Indeed, the current flowing under these conditions could be shown accurately equivalent to the net sodium-ion transport. Hence the potential difference is produced by the sodium transport, rather than sodium transport by the potential difference.

## Relationship between secretion and concentrative uptake by cells

The membrane-of-cells experiment of Oxender described on page 31 also supports the view that secretion or transcellular transport is produced by the ordinary concentrative activity of plasma membranes, which has somehow been made to operate more vigorously at one portion of the boundary of the secretory cell than at another. Figure 15 presents this concept. If the uphill transport can be caused to be more vigorous from side A than from side B, while the escape remains equal in both directions, uphill transport from side A to side B will result.

This view is an extension of the suggestion of Koefoed-Johnson and Ussing (1953) that an uphill extrusion of sodium ion occurs from the interior side, whereas only a mediated migration occurs at the cornified exterior side of the germinal cell layer in frog skin to produce the characteristic uphill transport of sodium ion across this tissue. In the case of intestinal absorption, the well-documented

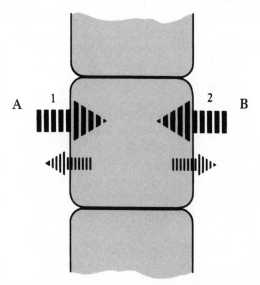

**Figure 15** Diagram to show how the uptake processes of epithelial cells might produce secretion. A and B are two extracellular phases separated by a layer of cells. The larger arrows for solute entry and the smaller arrows for exit serve to illustrate that the steady-state concentration of the solute will be higher in the cells than in either extracellular phase. Any process that will accelerate entry process 1, or slow entry process 2, will cause uphill transport from phase A to phase B. [*From Oxender, D. L., and Christensen, H. N.* (1959), *J. Biol. Chem.,* **234,** 2323; *with permission.*]

uphill transport of amino acids and sugars from the mucosal to the serosal side may well arise from the presence of an entry by active transport and an exit by facilitated diffusion; or it may arise instead from the presence of many more transport sites or carriers for uphill transport in the increased surface of the brush border, which mucosal cells expose to the lumen, than on the opposite poles of these cells; or from greater delivery of energy to the sites at the brush border. For the amino acids at least, the latter explanation seems more likely. Figure 16 represents the brush border.

Among the amino acids, a strong similarity in the specificity of the intestinal transport system, on the one hand, and of the systems of the red blood cell and the Ehrlich cell, on the other, is illustrated

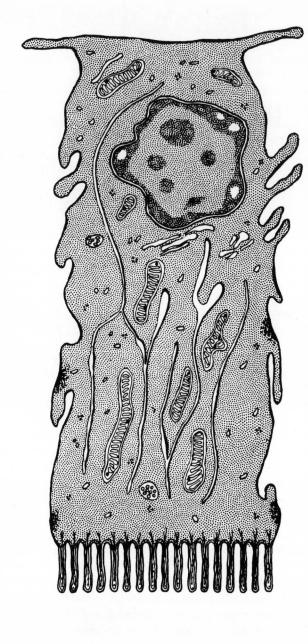

**Figure 16** A schematic drawing of a cylindrical epithelial cell lining the small intestine of the mouse, showing the so-called brush border. [*From Sjøstrand, F. S., in J. L. Oncley (ed.), Biophysical Science: A Study Program, Wiley, New York, 1959, p. 313; with permission.*]

in Table 1. The structural requirements for transport are highly similar. Among the neutral amino acids with hydrocarbon side-

Table 1   Similarity of the Sequences of Initial Uptake Rates of Amino Acids by Isolated Cells and by Intestinal Tissue [a]

| Amino acid | Human erythro-cytes,[b] $\mu M$/ml cell water/min | Ehrlich cell,[c] $\mu M$/ml cell water/min | Rat intestine [d] | |
|---|---|---|---|---|
| | | | $\mu M$/g dry wt/min | Apparent $K_m$, M/L |
| Glycine | 0.002 | 0.72 | 0.7 | 34 |
| L-Alanine | 0.004 | 2.7 | 2.8 | 5.0 |
| L-Valine | 0.14 | 2.0 | 3.4 | 2.1 |
| L-Leucine | 0.27 | 2.3 | 3.5 | 0.65 |

[a] All rates were observed at approximately 1 m$M$ external concentrations. Finch and Hird (1960) have shown that the rates for uptake by and transport across the intestine are closely correlated. The inhibitory effects of the amino acids on the intestinal transport of various neutral amino acids increase in the same order (cf. Wiseman, 1954).

[b] The results on red blood cells were obtained by Winter (1962).

[c] Results on Ehrlich cells are from Oxender (1962b).

[d] Results on intestine were obtained by Finch and Hird (1960).

chains, the higher affinity (more rapid transport; stronger inhibitory action) is shown in these three instances by those with large lipophilic sidechains. A discontinuity appears in each case so that the lower-affinity amino acids, glycine and $\alpha$-aminoisobutyric acid, suffer much less competition than they should from the high-affinity members (Akedo and Christensen, 1962a). The origin of this discontinuity and also the exceptional rate shown by alanine in the Ehrlich cell will be discussed subsequently. The basic amino acids represent a different family for each process, with each family showing competition among its members but not for amino acids of different net charge. These identities of behavior support the fundamental similarities of the processes.

Agar et al. (1953; 1956) showed that everted intestinal sacs accumulate into the tissue the amino acids that are also concentrated into a saline solution placed in the serosal compartment. Finch and Hird (1960) extended this relationship to show similarity in the kinetics of saturation and inhibition for the two phenomena.

39

Because of this behavior, observations of the concentrative uptake of amino acids by intestinal tissue are conceded considerable validity from which to predict concentration across the mucosa and are often substituted experimentally for the latter. Parallel behavior for monosaccharides permits use of the same technique with them (Crane and Mandelstam, 1960). Similarly, the ability of the kidney tubule to reabsorb galactose has been related to the ability of kidney slices to accumulate this sugar (Krane and Crane, 1959). In a number of other cases, solutes have been shown to be accumulated into a secreting tissue prior to or in association with their secretion. The over-all conclusion is that the secretory process probably utilizes the transport capabilities attributed to the plasma membrane of most cells.

## Pinocytosis and membrane flow

Warren Lewis discovered in 1931 that cells in tissue culture form invaginations along their periphery and that these invaginations are frequently pinched off to become vacuoles. He called the behavior "pinocytosis" and likened it to a drinking of extracellular fluid by the cells. This possible mode of transport has received increased interest from the observation that insulin has been reported to increase the frequency of invagination of the cells of the rat epididymal fat pad, in association with the increased rate of uptake of glucose (Barrnett and Ball, 1960).

Prohibitive difficulties appear, however, to stand in the way of accounting for many of the rapid, mediated transports of small solute molecules by pinocytosis. Such a nonspecific inclusion of extracellular fluid would appear to produce more transport problems than it solves, since huge volumes would need to be engulfed to account for the amounts of some solutes taken up. In addition, almost all other solute molecules, and the water, would then need to be discharged from the cell. Moreover, the specificity of transport would be unexplained and the kinetic observations entirely unaccounted for. The possibility that extracellular fluid enters cisternae formed by endoplasmic reticulum has already been mentioned; this arrangement, if it exists, might serve to increase the area available for transport into and out of cells.

A distinct yet related concept supposes that the cell membrane flows into a sink, so that portions steadily enter the interior of the cell (Bennett, 1956). Goldacre (1952) had suggested that the plasma membrane participates in the contraction-relaxation cycle of proto-plasmic streaming. The membrane was supposed by Bennett to carry with it certain solute molecules fixed to specific acceptor sites. Observations with ameba have contributed to this concept (Holter, 1959). All measurements of the frequency of occurrence of acceptor sites on the cell surface have indicated such astonishingly low values, however, that enormous rates of flow of the membrane would be necessary to account, for example, for the potassium-ion taken up by the red blood cell. Apparently a section of membrane no less than 1,000 by 1,000 by 70 A thick would be necessary for each potassium ion taken up or exchanged. One finds it hard to believe that the cells have access to enough energy to exchange their cations as rapidly as they do in this way, even if all the membrane taken into the cell is preserved to become exterior again. Furthermore, many cytologists now question the earlier concept that deep in-foldings of plasma membrane into the cell are a common or gen-eral occurrence.

Engulfment by invagination and vacuolization may very well apply to particulate matter and also to large molecules such as the proteins that have been shown to be able to enter and leave cells. Solutes that are otherwise excluded from the cell may also gain access whenever particulates are being engulfed; this behavior oc-curs for erythrose diphosphate when polystyrene particles are en-gulfed by macrophage cells (Karnovsky and Sbarra, 1959).

### Group translocation

Figure 17 shows a scheme proposed by Mitchell and Moyle (1958a, 1958b) to show how a phosphoryl group could be donated by ATP, by way of a phosphokinase, to phosphorylate a substrate S. In this scheme, the enzyme is pictured as part of a membrane, so that the chemical transfer of the phosphoryl group also translocates this group from one phase to another. The active site of the enzyme is visualized as lying at a cleft in the barrier, so that it is accessible from both sides; but steric features lead at least one of the substrates to tend to approach the site more readily from one side than from the other, thus establishing net translocation in one direction. Mitchell has discussed also net translocation of the succinyl group and of amino-acyl residues by similar hypothetical systems.

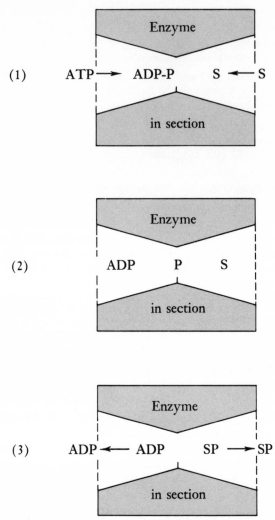

**Figure 17** The possible role of an enzyme in a group translocation. See text for details. [*From Mitchell, P., and Moyle, J.* (1958), *Nature,* **182,** 373; *with permission.*]

The essential element emphasized by these authors is that ordinary enzymes appropriately situated between phases may serve to transfer groups from one phase to another and, with an appropriate energy input, create concentration gradients.

These special features of position and configuration could perhaps be attributed equally well to proteins that are not ordinary enzymes and which accomplish the vectorial part of the transfer with only a transient chemical alteration. Specific binding sites are recognized to occur on protein molecules possessing little or no catalytic activity. We shall consider later whether the specificity patterns of transport suggest that ordinary enzymes contribute specific transport sites.

Group translocations may perhaps also be effected from peptides, which in some instances appear to donate a contained free amino acid to cells (Gale and Van Halteren, 1952; Leach and Snell, 1959, 1960; Newey and Smyth, 1959a, 1959b). The peptide cleavage does not occur outside the cell. If the peptidase is located in the plasma membrane and if it releases one of the hydrolysis products into the cell, we may say that the enzyme has mediated a group translocation.

## Definition of transport

The transfer of chemical groups from a donor to an acceptor and, at the same time, from one phase to another is a subject that certainly lies in the area of our biological interest in transport. Furthermore, the proposal by Mitchell and Moyle concerning this type of enzyme behavior stands as one of the important suggestions as to how the actual vectorial component of transport may perhaps be achieved. From the physicochemical point of view, however, an important distinction needs to be made between group translocations per se and the events that have classically been understood as transports.

Historically, central interest in transport has gone to the challenging problem—how a solute can be propelled from one phase into another against a concentration gradient, as in the secretion process. This interest focused careful attention on the reality of the gradient, that is, on the identity of the states of the migrating solute in the two phases. The realization then followed that inherently similar processes might operate across a barrier between phases without producing gradients. The broadened interest nevertheless remained in the transfer of a distinct molecular species. Let me therefore urge, without any wish to set arbitrary limits to the scope of our biological interest, that we continue to define transport as the process by which a solute is transferred from one phase to another, being in the same initial and final states in both phases. This terminologic question is considered further in Appendix 1.

Although we should intuitively like the term *transport* to imply that something is conveyed from one place to another, the more closely we describe a given biological transport the less able we may be to see an actual act of transport occurring at any stage. Transport could possibly occur simply by an association reaction followed by the diffusion of the product into the cell and its eventual dissociation to yield the original solute. If neither the association nor the dissociation reaction has a vectorial character, migration may occur solely by diffusion of the solute-carrier complex; only by considering that the sequence occurs consecutively to produce a result we are trying to explain does it appear to us as a specific transport. An example that comes to mind concerns the concentration of iodide by a sea weed. Shaw (1959) proposed that iodide is oxidized to iodine extracellularly, and that elementary iodine or HIO diffuses into the cells, where it is again reduced to iodide to be trapped there. As in this instance, transport as we understand it intuitively may tend to disappear when we look at the process stage by stage. As in the proverb, we see the golden eggs only if we retain the goose intact. Perhaps only if it should be proved that solutes are pulled through the barrier by a mechanical change in the shape of a protein molecule should we be satisfied that a crucial transport step has been identified. Unless transport is of such a mechanical character, analysis may cause any identifiable transport step to disappear.

# 3

〰〰〰〰〰〰〰〰〰〰

# *Kinetic approach to transport*

In the preceding chapter the reader may have observed how many of the present conceptions of transport have flowed from observations of the relationships of the rates of migration of a substance to its concentration and to the concentration of analogs and inhibitors. A brief consideration follows of the relationships to be expected, assuming that transport occurs in some of the ways considered in the last chapter.

## Diffusion

We have already seen that the rate for net diffusion occurring over a given area of membrane is given by

$$V = K_D(S_1 - S_2) \tag{1}$$

That is, the rate is governed by the nature of the membrane and of the permeant as represented by the diffusion constant, and by the concentration gradient.

## Chemical mediation

If a mediation or facilitation of diffusion occurs whereby the solute combines transiently with a mediating structure C to form a complex CS, which redissociates after passing through the barrier, the rate should still be given by

$$V = K_D(CS_1 - CS_2) \tag{2}$$

Unfortunately, however, the gradient of the solute-carrier complex is not an available quantity.

In terms of the solute concentration, the *unidirectional flux* across a membrane by a process utilizing a site or carrier of limited capacity could be expected to be given by the equation of Michaelis and Menten:

$$V = V_{max} \frac{S}{S + K_m} \tag{3}$$

Several assumptions need, however, to be made. The rate-limiting step must be neither the association of C and S nor the dissociation of CS but, instead, the translational event presumably separating these events. The diffusion constants must be the same for C and CS. To obtain a unidirectional flux, the initial rate must be measured, or at least the level of the solute on the other side of the membrane must be low compared with the $K_m$ applying for transport from that side. According to the usual procedure for testing for applicability of these relationships, a plot of $1/V$ against $1/S$ will be linear when the equation applies, and the two parameters $V_{max}$ and $K_m$ can then be determined as usual (see textbook discussions of enzyme kinetics).

For net transport in a system not able to transport the solute uphill, the net migration rate will be given by

$$V = V_{max} \left( \frac{S_1}{S_1 + K_m} - \frac{S_2}{S_2 + K_m} \right) \tag{4}$$

Here, $K_m$ has been assumed the same for the transports in the two directions. Wilbrandt and Rosenberg (1961) call attention to the expectation that, under the foregoing assumptions, $K_m$ but not $V_{max}$ may be expected to vary for a group of different but analogous substrates. Sen and Widdas (1962) evaluated carefully $V_{max}$ for D-glucose and D-mannose for red cell transport and found essentially identical values. They also measured carefully the effects of temperature and pH on $K_m$ and $V_{max}$.

Equation (4) may be rearranged for convenience to the form

$$V = V_{\max} \frac{(S_1 - S_2)K_m}{(S_1 + K_m)(S_2 + K_m)} \tag{4a}$$

Wilbrandt (1956) pointed out that, under limiting conditions of solute concentration, Equation (4a) predicts contrasting characteristics for the system. When $S_1$ and $S_2$ are well below saturation (small compared with $K_m$), the usual expectation will be realized that solutes showing highest affinity will be most rapidly transported. In this case, the denominator of Equation (4a) approaches the square of $K_m$. The rate therefore becomes proportional to the gradient, as for diffusion. This derivation also shows mathematically what one can grasp intuitively, that diffusion-type kinetics never exclude chemical mediation in transport, because the capacity of the mediator may be higher than the highest levels that have been tested or that can be tested.

On the other hand, if the concentrations on the two sides of the membrane are much larger than $K_m$, Equation (4a) approaches the form

$$V = V_{\max} K_m \left( \frac{1}{S_2} - \frac{1}{S_1} \right) \tag{5}$$

Equation (5) shows the velocity becoming directly proportional to $K_m$, which means that the solute with the higher affinity (and hence the lower $K_m$) will, at such high levels, be the one to reach equilibrium more slowly. One can grasp this intuitively by understanding that, at high saturation levels, the high-affinity solute will rarely permit a transport site to become vacant to transport a new solute molecule.

Historically, many solutes now known to enter uphill transports were earlier supposed not to be transported at all, simply because the tests were first made at levels too high in relation to the capacity of the system. Red blood cells were initially thought not to admit most amino acids. It was the author's experience to conclude initially that $\beta$-chloroalanine is scarcely transported at all into the Ehrlich cell (Riggs *et al.*, 1954), whereas its affinity actually is so high as to minimize uphill transport except at rather low levels.

Rosenberg and Wilbrandt (1957) used sugar transport into red blood cells to verify the above conclusion. Subsequently, Finch and Hird (1960) showed the applicability of the concept to the concentrative uptake of amino acids by sections of small intestine, although this situation must be kinetically more complex. In Figure 18 the rates at 1-m$M$ levels are plotted from the data of Finch and Hird (1960) against those obtained at 10 m$M$. The tendency for the sequence of rates to be reversed (excepting for glycine) is obvious. The exceptional positions of glycine and $\alpha$-aminoisobutyric acid on such a plot have been mentioned earlier.

More complex kinetic treatment has been proposed for the cases in which an enzyme may be necessary for the formation and dissociation of the solute-carrier complex (Wilbrandt and Rosenberg, 1961).

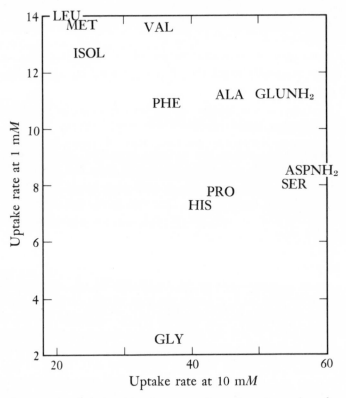

**Figure 18** Relationships between the rates of uptake of amino acids at 1- and 10-m$M$ levels by intestinal tissue. [*Data of Finch, L. R., and Hird, J. F. R.* (1960), *Biochim. et Biophys. Acta*, **43**, 268.]

## Systems with concentrative capabilities

Uphill transport can be produced by withdrawing the carrier at one side of the membrane and supplying it at the other, as is considered to occur when a flow is driven by a counterflow. Or it can be visualized as being caused by a change in the affinity produced through a modification in the chemical structure of the carrier at one face of the membrane, as illustrated later in Figure 23. In either case, the effective $K_m$, the level of solute producing half-saturation of transport, is modified. The appropriate form of Equation (4) then becomes

$$V = V_{\max}\left(\frac{S_1}{S_1 + K_1} - \frac{S_2}{S_2 + K_2}\right) \tag{6}$$

The ratio of the two values of $K_m$ defines the maximal distribution ratio that the transport can produce.

Obviously, if the affinity of the carrier is to be increased in such a way that uphill transport will result, energy must be received from an exergonic reaction. Part of this energy is then presumed to become available, as the affinity is again decreased, to permit dissociation of the modified carrier-solute complex to generate elevated levels of the solute. The increase in the $K_m$ of the carrier may be produced equally well before or after the dissociation; if it occurs afterward, the reversal of the dissociation is decreased to a corresponding degree.

When the kinetics of escape of solutes from cells are approximately linear, the assumption has often been made that the uphill transport is opposed by diffusion and that the steady state finds the active transport exactly balanced by leakage. Wilbrandt and Rosenberg (1961) have also derived kinetic equations for this case. The implication of this assumption is that the carrier has been removed completely or modified in a way to make the affinity negligible, or the value of $K_m$ infinite. But if $K_m$ has instead been increased only moderately, the cellular levels tested may still not have been high enough to demonstrate the mediation of exit. The general equation [see Equation (6)] should remain applicable to this case.

49

## Migration by more than one process

As the level of a solute is increased, one frequently finds that the rate does not entirely stop increasing; instead it still continues to increase gradually in a linear fashion, as illustrated in Figure 19. This result shows that at least two processes participate, one saturable and one that fails to saturate within the range of study. (The latter probably includes not only diffusion but also, or instead, a hard-to-saturate passive mediation, like the process seen above to participate in the escape of amino acids from cells.) A situation of this kind has been studied for the isolated diaphragm in its uptake of radioactive α-aminoisobutyric acid in the presence or absence of added insulin (see Figure 19) (Akedo and Christensen, 1962b).

In his analysis, Akedo separated these two components by integrating the equation giving the total flux as the sum of two fluxes:

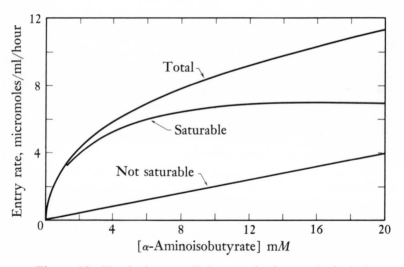

**Figure 19** Uptake by two distinct mechanisms. α-Aminoisobutyrate entry into the isolated rat diaphragm *in vitro*. The upper curve shows the total rate of uptake (corrected for entry into the inulin space) as a function of the extracellular concentration. The middle curve shows the calculated rate of the saturable process; the lower curve, of the process not subject to saturation up to 0.1 *M*. [*Results of Akedo, H., and Christensen, H. N.* (1962), *J. Biol. Chem.*, **237**, 1180.]

$$\frac{dA_2}{dt} = Y + K_D(A_1 - A_2) \tag{7}$$

where $Y$ is the rate of the saturable component. Under the assumption that $A_1$ had been kept constant by the use of a large volume of suspending solution, and that the rate of the saturable component $Y$ is independent of time and of the intracellular concentration, $A_2$, Equation (7) can be integrated to give

$$\frac{A_2}{A_1} = \frac{Y(1 - e^{-K_D t})}{K_D}\frac{1}{A_1} + (1 - e^{-K_D t}) \tag{8}$$

Now, at high extracellular concentrations, the saturable process will be saturated, and $Y$ will be very nearly constant. Therefore, the last term $(1 - e^{-K_D t})$ will be the intercept of a straight line relating $1/A_1$ and the distribution ratio $A_2/A_1$ at sufficiently high extracellular concentrations. By evaluating this term $(1 - e^{-K_D t})$ graphically, $K_D$, the apparent diffuson constant, was evaluated and introduced into Equation (8). The value of $Y$, the rate of the saturable component, could then be determined, and was found indeed to be nearly independent of time during the interval of study. As the concentration increased from 1 to 20 m$M$, the saturable component of the entry rate in the presence of insulin fell from 99 to 61 per cent of the total entry rate (Figure 19). The saturable component was shown further to follow Michaelis-Menten kinetics. In the absence of insulin, similar relationships held, except that $K_m$ appeared to be 10 times as large, whereas $V_m$ and $K_D$ were not measurably changed.

## Inhibition

Transport inhibitors, such as 2,4-dinitrophenol, cyanide, azide, and iodoacetate, interfere with the energy supply for transport, and probably do not react at all in the transport process. A more interesting type of inhibitor is one with an affinity for the same site at which the solute is accepted in a mediated transport, and with no other action on the transport system. Both among the amino acids and among the sugars (and apparently also among the lower fatty acids, anions, the purines, and other classes), we find whole families of solutes reacting, each with their specific transport site, with affinities falling in sequences that permit informative study.

Wilbrandt and Rosenberg (1961) supplied a kinetic equation for the competition of such an inhibitor with the substrate for combination with the carrier, specifically for an inhibitor that reaches the same concentration on the two sides of the membrane:

$$V = V_{max}\left(\frac{S'_1}{S'_1 + I' + 1} - \frac{S'_2}{S'_2 + I' + 1}\right) \tag{9}$$

$S'$ and $I'$ are the relative concentrations of the solute and the inhibitor, with reference to the relevant value of $K_m$:

$$S' = \frac{S}{K_m} \quad \text{and} \quad I' = \frac{I}{K_I}$$

For application to uphill transport, different values of $K_m$ should presumably be used for each of the two directions of flux. These authors show that this equation requires that the inhibitor will not only inhibit at higher levels, but that it will also accelerate transport by driving exchange at relatively low levels in the manner shown earlier by Heinz and Walsh (1958). A sequence of initial inhibition followed by acceleration can arise in the more complex but practical situation where the inhibitor is initially placed in one phase only, and then is itself concentrated into the other phase. Experiments, to be described in the next chapter, indicate that $K_1/K_2$ may be very different for different amino acids, i.e., that one amino acid may lose much more apparent affinity than another through carrier modification, complicating the problem still further, whether the net effect will be an inhibition or stimulation of uptake.

In this connection, Jacquez (1961) has introduced the use of a computer to test the kinetic requirements of various models for amino acid transport.

# 4

~~~~~~~~~~~~~~~~~~~~~

# *Specificity of transport*

## General

The minimal requirement of a chemical site mediating transport, under the simplest conception, is that it be able to bind the transported solute in such a way that it can be released into either of two phases. We can study transport, as we study the specificity of binding by an enzyme or other protein, by examining analogous solute molecules to see if they appear to be transported by the same site, and by proceeding to structures less and less similar to the solute until we encounter structural modifications that eliminate affinity for the transport site. In this way we should be able to map the active site.

For enzymes, we have come to expect rather high (although not necessarily absolute) structural and steric specificity in the binding of substrate molecules and in the consequent catalytic action on them. For comparison with transport sites we should perhaps limit the analogy with enzymes to the specificity of binding and not to their action as catalysts; the requirements are then obviously not as high. On the other hand, we can sense that transport may also introduce additional specificity requirements. In the simplest case, if the solute does not readily dissociate from the site, no significant transport will occur; this situation is analogous to the inhibition produced when the product of an enzymatic catalysis fails to dissociate from the enzyme. We have seen also that complex events may intervene between the binding and release of the solute, so that if we measure the rate of transport we may get a different comparison between solutes than if we use stoichiometric binding to a receptor site.

The comparison between the active sites of enzymes and those of transport mediators needs to be made cautiously until the operation of each is understood.

If we consider, in turn, various groups of solutes undergoing transport, the *metal ions* offer us very limited opportunities to use comparison among analogs to study the nature of binding sites involved, because usually only one analog even approaches a fit (rubidium for potassium ion, strontium for calcium ion, manganese for magnesium ion, lithium, in some cases, for sodium ion). Apparently in some cases, the ammonia ion, amines, and even amino acids can compete with the alkali metals for transport (cf. Conway and Duggan, 1958). These structures are so diverse that one wonders whether they actually compete for the same chemical site.

### Specificity of glycerol transport

The site serving as the portal of entry for glycerol into the human red blood cell operates also for 1,2,4-trihydroxybutane, but not for erythritol. The tetrahydroxy compound apparently belongs to the domain of monosaccharide transport. The propanediols, especially 1,3-propanediol, are inhibitors of glycerol transport, although they are so lipophilic as to enter the red blood cells without obvious mediation. A small slowing of 1,2-propanediol entry by cupric ion has been observed, indicating that a small part of its entry probably is mediated. Ethylene glycol and even ordinary alcohols show some ability to inhibit glycerol transport, more than would be expected nonspecifically from their entry into lipid phases.

### Specificity of amino acid transport

The amino acids probably offer the largest series of analogous structures for study, particularly since almost all the "neutral" or monoamino, monocarboxylic members seem to show some affinity for a common site or sites. Given that the product contains the $\alpha$-amino and $\alpha$-carboxyl group, it has been difficult to discover structural alterations on the amino acid sidechain that abolish transport, as long as a new positive or negative charge is not introduced. Furthermore, the inhibitory action of a variety of amino acids of abnormal structure indicates that they use the same transport sites as the normal amino acids do. Accordingly, we shall note some strange amino acids in use for the study of normal amino acid transport.

The anionic amino acids, on the one hand, and the cationic amino acids, on the other, appear to represent transport families distinct from the neutral amino acids in that inhibitions occur only within each group and not between the three groups. Conceivably, sites of a similar nature could serve for all three families, except that some might be shielded from approach of an anionic or a cationic amino acid by the presence of a nearby charged group. This simple view is doubted for the dicarboxylic amino acids, however, since, for the Ehrlich cell, the presence of an $\alpha$-methyl group on the amino acid blocks the transport of the dicarboxylic but not of the neutral amino acids (Christensen, 1955). The presence of the $\gamma$-amide group, as in glutamine, makes an $\alpha$-methyl group again acceptable.

Among the diamino acids, a very interesting, intense augmentation of transport occurs when the omega amino group is brought close enough to the $\alpha$-amino group. Whereas ornithine undergoes only a mildly concentrative uptake, $\alpha,\gamma$-diaminobutyric acid is accumulated to an extent that can be destructive to the cell (Christensen et al., 1952b).

A clear affinity sequence for the rates of uptake of the neutral amino acids having aliphatic hydrocarbon sidechains and for their inhibitory action has been observed in the human erythrocyte (where the uptake apparently is not concentrative), also in the Ehrlich ascites tumor cell, and in the everted sac of the rat intestine, a useful experimental preparation introduced by Wilson and Wiseman (1954). In this sequence glycine has the least affinity, alanine next, followed by valine and leucine in order. The same sequence of affinities is shown in the strength of their ability to drive the exchange uptake of susceptible amino acids.

These results imply that the hydrocarbon sidechain of these amino acids may be involved as a third point of binding, in addition to the amino and carboxyl groups, which have so far proved specifically necessary for the characteristic interaction. Presumably the hydrocarbon sidechains could join to a third locus at the transport

55

site by an apolar bond. The direction of this bond is probably not especially critical, since hydrocarbon groups of various lengths and branchings can serve. Perhaps the small but definite affinity shown by the D isomers (about one-tenth that shown by their L enantiomorphs) arises from a degree of flexibility in the direction of this third point of attachment. Conceivably, the large hydrocarbon groups, rather than serving statically as a third point of attachment, could facilitate the passage or creeping of the solute molecules from one polar site to another, by bonding transiently to corresponding hydrocarbon sites in the membrane.

As Figure 20 shows, however, the whole story of the uptake of neutral amino acids by the Ehrlich cell is more complex than the two preceding paragraphs may have suggested. The curve marked *Leucine* shows how quickly the amino acids with large hydrocarbon

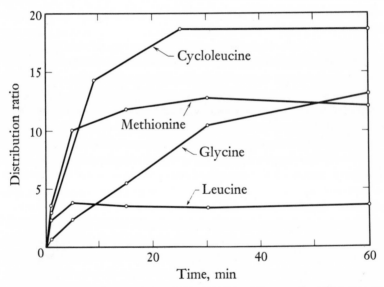

**Figure 20**  Time course of the uptake of four amino acids by the Ehrlich ascites tumor cell. The curve for α-aminoisobutyric acid uptake resembles that for glycine except that higher distribution ratios are reached. "Cycloleucine" designates 1-aminocyclopentanecarboxylic acid. [*From Christensen et al. (1962), in J. F. Holton (ed.), Conference on Free Amino Acids, Elsevier, Amsterdam; with permission.*]

sidechains enter and reach a steady state of distribution, whereas that marked *Glycine* shows the much lower initial rates for this amino acid. Despite this difference, however, glycine in the course of time reaches a much higher distribution ratio in favor of the cell interior than do L-leucine and L-valine, as has long been known (Christensen *et al.*, 1952a). The same is true for α-aminoisobutyric acid. Even though the entry rate for these two is relatively slow, their rate of exodus can be shown to be even slower, so that they eventually reach cellular levels over twenty times as high as the extracellular levels. In contrast, leucine and valine both enter and leave rapidly, so that high accumulations are never reached. Obviously these results cannot be explained by the action of a single mediating site; specifically, they require that the mediating structure by which amino acids escape have a selectivity among the amino acids different from the selectivity of the mediation by which they enter.

A similar difficulty is presented by comparisons between enantiomorphic pairs of amino acids. Ordinarily the L isomer, in terms of the initial rate of entry, has an affinity about ten times that of the D isomer. But gradually the D isomer reaches a distribution ratio at least half as high as that attained by the L isomer. Accordingly, the D isomer not only enters more slowly, but also leaves the cell more slowly than its antipode. Such results have been obtained with several enantiomorphic pairs. One cannot readily conceive that two optical antipodes would diffuse out at different rates. Thus, even if all the D-isomer escape occurred by simple diffusion, clearly a major fraction of the escape of the L isomers must be mediated to explain their much faster exodus. At least some D-alanine escape, however, appears also to be mediated, since it shows competitive inhibition of L-alanine exit (Oxender, 1962b).

But if the cell has a separate passive mediator by which the neutral amino acids escape from its interior, why should this mediator not work in the opposite direction and participate also in their entry? Accordingly, one should be able to detect entry by two mediators with different affinity patterns. By observing the extent to which each of a number of neutral amino acids inhibits the uptake of others, Oxender (1962a, 1962b) has shown that their entry occurs by two different sites with overlapping affinities. The first of these has already been described in part; it shows high selectivity for amino acids with large hydrocarbon sidechains. Its approximate properties are tentatively summarized in Table 2. It is also only moderately stereospecific. It operates rapidly in both directions; at the present we do not know whether it can operate uphill or represents only a facilitated diffusion.

The other site, tentatively designated $A$, apparently operates for entry only and shows good affinity for L-alanine, $\alpha$-aminoisobutyric acid, and glycine, decreasing in that order. When the hydrocarbon chain is lengthened, and particularly when it is branched at $C_3$ as in valine, affinity for this site is rapidly lost; the entry of valine at a 5-m$M$ level appears to occur only to a minor extent by this site. If the apolar sidechain is not branched, with further lengthening a secondary increase in affinity for the $A$ site occurs, as can be illustrated with norleucine and methionine. Apparently the ethereal sulfur in methionine is roughly equivalent to a methyl-

**Table 2 Tentative Summary of Characteristics of Two Transport Mediators for Neutral Amino Acids as Identified in the Ehrlich Cell**

| Characteristic | Site $A$ | Site $L$ |
|---|---|---|
| Steady-state distribution ratios | High (10 to 20) | Low (1 to 3) |
| Availability for exodus and for exchange | Poor, if at all | Free |
| Sensitivity to alkali metal ions | Strong | Weak |
| Temperature sensitivity; $Q_{10}$ (27 to 37°) | ca. 3.5 | ca. 2.5 |
| Stereospecificity | Partial | Partial |
| Sensitivity to deficiency in energy supply | High | Minimal |
| Present in adult human erythrocyte | Minimal | Predominant |

ene group in this matter. This relationship appears to explain why methionine has good affinity for both sites, and why in Figure 20 it shows not only a high initial rate but also high accumulation into the cell. It shows strong competitive action for both sites, a factor that may explain the unusual toxicity of elevated plasma levels of this amino acid.

When allowance is made for entry through the $A$ site by glycine, $\alpha$-aminoisobutyric acid, and alanine, very little of the relatively slow entry of α-aminoisobutyric acid and glycine (as illustrated in Figure 20), and rather little of the alanine entry, remain for assignment to the valine-preferring site. When this correction is made, the fall-off in relative affinity of this site in the series valine, alanine, and glycine is essentially as steep as it is in the mature human erythrocyte (Table 1, page 39). The aberrant affinity for alanine uptake in the Ehrlich cell shown in this table, compared with intestinal transport and uptake by the red blood cell, appears to be explained by the dominance of the $A$ site in the Ehrlich cell. At the reticulocyte stage rabbit erythrocyte concentrates glycine actively (Riggs *et al.*, 1952); hence a mediation resembling the $A$ site must be present at that stage; but the amino acid transport shown by the mature erythrocyte corresponds very closely to the affinity of the valine-preferring mediator. The behavior of glycine, alanine, and α-aminoisobutyric acid in intestinal transport and in their uptake by the isolated diaphragm of the rat (Akedo and Christensen, 1962a; 1962b), as well as their uptake by bacteria (Marquis, 1961; Mora, 1961), suggests that this dichotomy in the transport of the neutral amino acids may be very widespread. It will be interesting to know how the two mediations are distributed between the opposite faces of secretory cells, as in the intestinal mucosa.

Whereas most of the entry of glycine and α-aminoisobutyric acid into the Ehrlich cell occurs by the apparently oneway $A$ site, their exodus appears to occur by the other, valine-preferring site, despite the unfavorable affinity (Figure 21a). That is, these amino acids appear to accumulate in the cell until their concentrations there are high enough to compensate for their unfavorable affinities for this mediator.

Although alanine has the better affinity for the $A$ site, α-aminoisobutyric acid is a better solute for investigation of this mediator, because its selectivity between the two sites is almost completely in favor of this one ($A$). Such a dual-affinity amino acid as methionine could conceivably play a special role in transport by being strongly accumulated by the $A$ site, the accumulations then serving in turn for exchange in the valine-preferring mediation to cause considerable uphill transport of such amino acids as leucine and valine (Figure 21b). As shown in Figure 20, 1-aminocyclopentanecarboxylic acid has a course of uptake like that for methionine, and similar affinity for the two sites. This situation makes it an interesting trans-

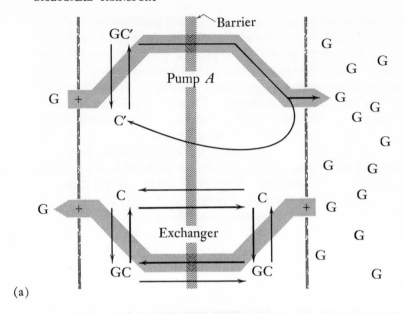

(a)

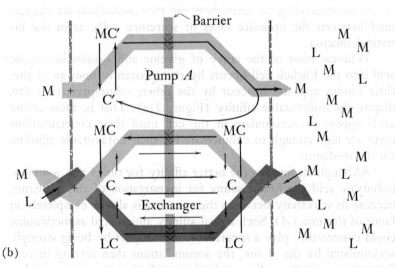

(b)

**Figure 21** A visualization of the possible operation of dissimilar mediators (C and C′): (a) for entry and exodus of an amino acid such as glycine; (b) for an amino acid such as methionine to permit it to drive the uphill transport of, for example, leucine.

port model. For observing the valine-preferring mediation in isolation, the difficultly metabolized pseudoleucine (tertiary leucine) appears a promising model amino acid.

Figure 22 shows a possible scheme by which two transport mediators discussed above could conceivably be related. The media-

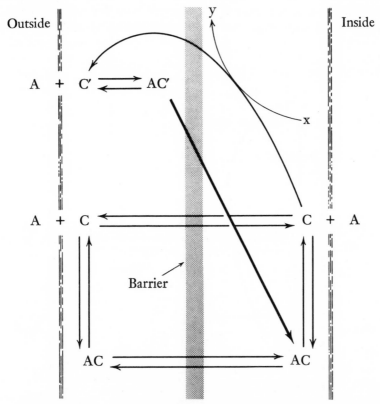

**Figure 22**   A possible scheme for amino acid transport. C is a transport site or carrier; A, an amino acid molecule. C′ is a more reactive form of the transport site, generated perhaps by the exergonic reaction, $x \rightarrow y$. Reaction of A with C′ causes not only complexing but also triggers a structural change that places the complex CA inside the osmotic barrier (indicated by the shaded band). (Note that A is used here to represent the solute molecule and has nothing to do with the hypothetical *A* site of the Ehrlich cell.)

tor preferring alanine, glycine, and α-aminoisobutyric acid is here designated C'. It is visualized as a reactive form of the other site. Its combination with amino acid A from outside triggers a translocation so that the resultant complex C'A appears, in orientation to the internal phase, in the reorganized form CA, which can dissociate to produce a higher level of A than existed in the external phase. The scheme supposes, however, that site C retains considerable affinity especially for certain amino acids such as L-leucine and L-valine, so that for these it can operate both for exit and entry. Amino acids such as glycine and α-aminoisobutyric acid have such

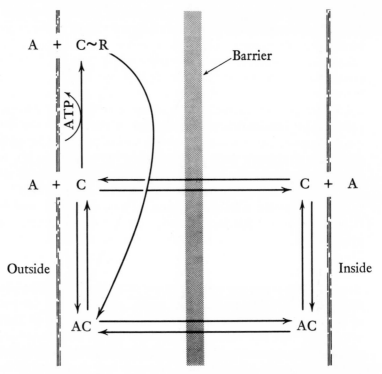

**Figure 23** Scheme for β-galactoside entry and exit, redrawn from Kepes (1960) to permit comparison with the scheme of Figure 22. The mode of activation of the carrier C is more closely specified in this case as the addition of R with a high-energy bond to C. R is then displaced by the entering solute molecule. In both schemes the lower sequence, $A + C \rightleftarrows AC \rightleftarrows AC \rightleftarrows C + A$, serves for passive migration.

relatively low affinities for C that, ordinarily, only when a large gradient has been established in favor of the cell interior is their exodus able to keep up with entry.

The scheme of Figure 22 should be related to an earlier one proposed by Kepes (1960) for the transport by *E. coli* of a group of three thio-$\beta$-galactosides, which proves to be quite similar. Kepes' scheme has been redrawn here (Figure 23) to facilitate comparison. Accumulation is considered to occur because an extra amount of the carrier-solute complex CA is formed outside the osmotic barrier by reaction of the external solute with a reactive form of the carrier, specified here to be C $\sim$ R. The solute displaces the radical R. The dissociation of CA may occur spontaneously. For the particular case of amino acid transport, the scheme of Figure 22 avoids the problem of retaining the high chemical potential of CA outside the osmotic barrier, in view of the leak represented by its direct outward release of A, by showing the carrier-solute complex transferred across the osmotic barrier as an immediate consequence of complex formation. This scheme also places the exergonic process driving uphill transport inside the cell. A direct stoichiometric linkage between ATP breakdown and activation of the carrier site should not be implied; such a direct linkage would probably be prohibitively wasteful since each ATP breakdown supplies several times the energy presumably required for transfer uphill of each amino acid molecule into the Ehrlich cell (Heinz and Patlak, 1960).

An alternative possibility is that the two chemically and functionally distinguishable mediators for the transfer of neutral amino acids are not two forms of the same carrier but are instead unrelated. Horecker *et al.* (1960; 1961) secured the induced formation of an exit process for galactose by an *E. coli* strain lacking a galactokinase. This bacterial strain has a constitutive, concentrative uptake process for galactose. The fact that the entry process could be present in the absence of the exit process appears discouraging to the possible view that the exit mediation was a part or a manifestation of the entry process. As the uptake process was suppressed by 2,4-dinitrophenol, however, the exit rate was increased. This behavior, which has also been observed for amino acids in the Ehrlich cell (cf. Christensen *et al.*, 1962), suggests that more of the exit-mediator is present when less energy is available for converting it into a form serving for uphill entry, as illustrated in Figure 22.

In this connection, we may recall again that the erythrocyte concentrates glycine strongly at the reticulocyte stage (Riggs *et al.*, 1952) but, at the adult stage, shows only a facilitated diffusion with high affinity for leucine and valine but with almost no affinity for glycine (Winter, 1962). This behavior suggests that the ability to render the carrier site reactive is largely lost on maturation of the erythrocyte as the energy supply available to the cell decreases, and perhaps argues also in favor of a generic relationship between the two mediating structures, such as that shown in Figure 22.

The foregoing examples show that a quantitative and not merely a qualitative demonstration is needed to establish that two solutes actually use exclusively the same mediation.

The transport of $\alpha$-aminoisobutyric acid illustrates that the presence of an alpha-hydrogen atom is not necessary to the transport of the neutral amino acids. Since the $\alpha$-hydrogen is necessary to many catabolic attacks on amino acids, many species do not metabolize such an amino acid, and it can therefore be used to study transport uncomplicated by irrelevant metabolic modifications. This approach has permitted the study of nutritional and endocrine influences (to be discussed in Chapter 8) on distribution and transport, without the possibility that these factors have primarily slowed or accelerated the formation or destruction of the amino acid, rather than transport.

In writing the following sentence in 1902, Rudolf Höber was supporting the use of organic compounds presenting a wide range of physical properties for the study of permeability: "When the foreign substances do not destroy the normal course of life processes, but when they instead pass through the organism uninjurious or unmodified, then their unusualness represents a distinct advantage for experimental study." In all fairness we must recognize that, in the cited discussion, Höber had not anticipated the use of structural analogs able to compete for a chemical mediation of transport.

A larger hydrocarbon structure, again occupying both the $\alpha_1$ and $\alpha_2$ positions in 1-aminocyclopentanecarboxylic acid, leads to much higher transport affinity than is shown for $\alpha$-aminoisobutyric acid. It also competes strongly with L-valine for the dissimilar site by which that amino acid enters the Ehrlich cell. If the cyclopentane ring is not closed between ring carbons numbered 3 and 4, that is, as in the analog $\alpha$-diethylglycine, we observe very little affinity for either site. Apparently, if the sidechain group at the position it characteristically occupies in D-amino acids is drawn by the ring structure away from the erect position it would otherwise tend to occupy, very large increases in transport affinity result. Extension of such structural comparisons promises to be highly informative as to the geometry of the amino acid transport sites. 1-Aminocyclopentanecarboxylic acid shows a high affinity for both intestinal (Akedo and Christensen, 1962a) and renal transport. The renal tubules resorb it so completely that, in the male rat or mouse, the amino acid cycles about in the body for many months (Christensen and Jones, 1962).

Genetically determined transport systems apparently limited to only one, two, or three neutral aliphatic amino acids rather than the whole group, have occasionally been reported for microorganisms, a pattern departing somewhat from the broader specificities shown by animal cells. The solutes of a class should be studied over very wide concentration ranges before concluding that no competitive actions occur among them.

## Specificity of sugar transport

A considerable number of monosaccharides are acceptable to the transport system of the human red blood cell. No successful generalization of the structural requirements for transport was reached until LeFevre and Marshall (1958) pointed out that the D-pyranoses with the highest transport affinity (D-glucose, 2-deoxy-D-glucose, 3-O-methyl glucose) are the ones having the most structural features tending to stabilize them in the chair conformation known as C1 (Figure 24). These are the sugars that appear on conformational analysis to have the highest number of (hydroxy + hydroxymethyl) groups in the equatorial orientation in the C1 form, but in the axial orientation in the other chair form, known as 1C. Passage of conformation from C1 form to 1C form is marked by the passage of all equatorially orientated groups (that is, extending outward from the rough plane described by the ring) to an axial orientation (that is, roughly perpendicular to the plane of the ring). The D-pyranoses with the lowest transport affinities are the ones that are not so unbalanced in the number of such groups in one orientation as in the other; these D-pyranoses are therefore almost as stable in one conformation as they are in the other.

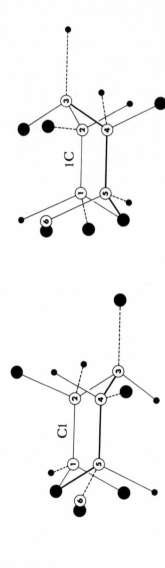

**Figure 24** Two chair conformations of α-ᴅ-mannose. The solid circle in the pyranose ring represents the oxygen atom. The larger solid circles outside the ring represent hydroxyl groups, and the smaller circles, hydrogen atoms. The heavy lines in the ring indicate the side facing the reader. Equatorial valences are shown by broken lines, axial valences by continuous lines. [*From LeFevre, P. G.* (1961), *Pharmacol. Revs.*, **13**, 47; *with permission.*]

*A priori* this type of specificity apparently could have three origins:

1. A mere equatorial orientation of a sufficient number of hydroxyl + hydroxymethyl groups about a chair ring could produce affinity. LeFevre and Marshall's study shows, however, that this factor cannot be sufficient, since, in contrast to the D-pyranoses most highly stabilized in the C1 conformation, their mirror-image L enantiomorphs are the sugars showing the *lowest* affinities. (Confusingly, these "all-equatorial" mirror-image forms are said to have the 1C conformation.)

(In the case of arabinose, it is the L form that shows the higher apparent stability of binding to the transport site, this being the enantiomorph having one more equatorial than axial substituents in the C1 conformation. Either enantiomorph of fucose is transported, the D form showing the higher affinity, in agreement with the same general criterion.)

2. Instead, an equatorial orientation of a sufficient number of hydroxyl + hydroxymethyl groups about one of the two possible chair rings (the one designated C1) seems to produce high affinity; around the other chair ring, low affinity.

3. Since a direct relationship has, however, not been established between transport affinity and the *fraction* of the pyranose existing in the favorable conformation, the factor unfavorable to transport could instead be a conformational flexibility, i.e., an ease of departure from the C1 conformation; or the structural features tending to stabilize the proper conformation could otherwise facilitate the interactions involved in transport.

To account for the observed preference, the cell membrane must have, in the words of these authors, "a systematic assembly of at least three contact points within a few Angstrom units of each other, in a fairly rigid pattern." Faust (1960) calls attention to a faster rate of passage at pH 7 and 8 for $\beta$-D-glucose than for $\alpha$-D-glucose and urges that various sugars must be compared in their mutarotated state. Comprehensive reviews of monosaccharide transport into red blood cells (LeFevre, 1961a), across the intestinal wall (Crane, 1960), and of sugars into microorganisms (Cirillo, 1961) are available.

The uphill transports of the intestine and the kidney discriminate more closely among monosaccharides than the red blood cell system does. The former have usually been explored with the everted-sac preparation. Intestinal transport of sugars requires a D-pyranose structure with a free hydroxyl group at position 2 in the same steric position it occupies in D-glucose, and a methyl or substituted methyl group representing carbon 6 (Wilson and Crane, 1958; Jorgensen *et al.*, 1961). The hydroxyl group at carbon 2 is the only one that is specifically necessary for affinity, since the others could be omitted or replaced one at a time. (The student may consider whether this means that mediation of transport would occur for an analog simultaneously lacking all four hydroxyl groups at carbons 1, 3, 4, and 6.) The way in which the transport system recognizes that the sugar is a pyranose of 6 carbons and has the required configuration has not been ascertained.

Two valuable muscular tissues for study of transport *in vitro* are the rat diaphragm, especially in the so-called "intact" form [including a section of the rib cage until incubation is complete (Kipnis and Cori, 1957)] and the perfused rat heart (Fisher and Lindsay, 1956). These two show very similar specificities for sugar transport, identical neither with the concentrative systems of the intestine or of the kidney nor with the passive uptake by the human erythrocyte, but rather more like the last. Affinity is shown for D-glucose, D-mannose, 2-deoxyglucose, and both D- and L-arabinose, among other sugars (Kipnis and Cori, 1959; Battaglia and Randle, 1960).

The technique of using solutes not easily metabolized in the tissue in question has also been useful in studying sugar transport, as well as for amino acid transport, as already described. The following may serve as examples: 3-*O*-methylglucose transport by various tissues introduced by Csaky (1938; 1942) in an early study of this kind (although at the time he sought only to prevent phosphorylation at position 3 by the presence of the methyl group); galactose uptake by kidney slices and into everted intestinal sacs (both transports concentrative in nature); ribose penetration into muscle; and thiogalactoside transport by *E. coli*.

This use of solutes obstructed to certain metabolic changes has also served to exclude several important suggestions as to how transport is produced. For example, the classic view that a given sugar transport occurs by phosphorylation at a certain position on the sugar molecule can be excluded by showing that transport occurs for a sugar lacking a hydroxyl group at the position in question. As another example, a few years ago uphill sugar transport was proposed to occur by means of the action of a mutarotase (Keston, 1954). This possibility was excluded by showing that the intestinal monosaccharide system transports the cyclic ether, 1-deoxyglucose, which is of course not subject to mutarotation (Crane and Krane, 1956).

Inhibitors not recognized to be transported may also assist in describing the site. Phloretin, the aglycone of phlorizin, inhibits the glucose transport system of human erythrocytes at least 50 times as strongly as phlorizin does. Phloretin, the free diphenol, is competitive in its action; both phenolic groups are necessary, and comparison of analogs has indicated that the magnitude of the spatial separation of these two hydroxyl groups is important. Accordingly, this distance may be an important parameter in the description of the monosaccharide transport site. Phloretin, as well as stilbestrol and other potent analogs of phloretin are, to complicate investigation, fixed by red blood cells at sites far more abundant than the transport sites (LeFevre and Marshall, 1959).

In contrast, it is phlorizin, the glycoside, that inhibits monosaccharide transport in the intestine and the kidney, and its entry into Ehrlich ascites tumor cells. Alvarado and Crane (1962) find phlorizin a competitive inhibitor for sugar transport into intestinal strips, phloretin being less than 1 per cent as active as the glycoside.

Findings on transport systems for organic anions in the kidney and in the diaphragm, and on transport systems for organic cations, could also be selected for a similar complementary consideration of the nature and function of the transport sites concerned. Similarly, the anions (thiocyanate, perchlorate, periodate, iodate, chlorate, hypochlorite, nitrate, nitrite, bromate, and numerous others) competing with iodide for transport by the thyroid, gastric, and salivary glands form an interesting series. Divalent cation transports (e.g., of sulfate by the kidney) are also known. Limited explorations have been made of the effect of structure on purine transport.

In summary, we may say that the transport of amino acids and sugars by their respective transport-mediating sites appears to occur for a wider range of molecular structures than can be handled by most enzymatic reactions. The patterns of specificity are sufficiently unlike those of most enzymes, suggesting that ordinary known enzymes in special locations are usually not the mediators of transport.

In this connection we should remember that transport also discriminates between solutes (e.g., the alkali metal ions) not subject to discriminating enzymatic attack. Elsewhere the author (1960b, 1961) has emphasized the possibility that transport sites occur in the matrix of the membrane structure rather than in small shuttling carriers. The specificities observed are those to be expected of sites formed by three or more chemical groups in a three-dimensional array. The membrane matrix could maintain a more closely determined arrangement of such groups than that possible for small molecules in free solution. Furthermore, translocation of such sites, and a decrease of affinity, or even an inversion in the order of affinities (as for the sodium and potassium ions), could be produced by close steric control of such three-dimensional binding sites, through structural changes akin to protein denaturation.

# 5

~~~~~~~~~~~~~~~~

# *Site isolation?*
# *Membrane separation*

Our main objective in the chemical approach to transport should be the identification of the reactive sites that mediate transports and the demonstration of their action in an isolated state. A very small number of transport-mediating groups appear to be able, in analogy to enzyme action, to transfer enormous numbers of solute molecules. Up to the present time, no procedures have succeeded in concentrating transport sites; or perhaps we should say more accurately, no efficient way is available for recognizing procedures able to concentrate transport sites or structures. Once the membrane is broken, unfortunately, we can expect to find at most only stoichiometric binding of the solute by the site, rather than the more sensitive indicator—mediation of transport, by which one site can operate for thousands of solute molecules. Therefore the sensitivity with which the site can be recognized probably falls, following cell breakage, by many orders of magnitude. The natural low concentration of such sites can be illustrated with the potassium transport site on the red blood cell estimated at one per every 1,000,-000 square Angstroms (Solomon *et al.*, 1956) or per every 10,000,-000 square Angstroms (Glynn, 1957b) of surface area. The latter value represents about 1,000 per cell. LeFevre set an upper limit to the number of glucose-transferring sites on the red blood cell ghost at 500,000 per cell, because he failed to detect any glucose binding, this value representing the sensitivity limit of his measurements.

An important approach is the search for end-group reagents that will stably mark transport sites on intact cells, so that isolative procedures will not dislodge the marker. Such reagents may perhaps be discovered by looking for irreversible inhibitors of transport. This approach has been illustrated above (page 20), by the report of Stein (1958), of an amino-terminal histidine on the red blood cell surface, whose reaction with phenylisothiocyanate is blocked by the inhibitor of glycerol transport, 1,3-propanediol. Again, because of the sparsity of such sites, unusual procedures are called for to make the marking sufficiently specific.

One may also hope that the isolation of transport sites might be monitored at each stage by examining for the specific binding properties corresponding to the pattern of solutes transported. Advantage would need to be taken of the aspects in which the characteristic specificity of the carrier differs from the specificity of known enzyme systems.

Attempts at the isolation of the plasma membrane are currently receiving substantial interest and effort. For the large cells of mammalian organisms, the amount of material comprising the plasma membrane cannot be large; for example, perhaps 0.25 per cent of the cell mass of the Ehrlich ascites tumor cell should represent the plasma membrane, taking the estimate of the electron microscopists (70 A) for the thickness of the membrane. A principal problem in the isolation of plasma membranes of many cells is their separation from other membraneous elements, particularly those of the endoplasmic reticulum. Some cytologists have interpreted parts of the reticulum either to represent infoldings of the plasma membrane or to be continuous with the plasma membrane. Palade wrote in 1956:

> Finally smooth surfaced profiles, similar to those belonging to the endoplasmic reticulum are found in close contact with the cell membrane in numerous cell types. Some of these profiles are closed whereas others appear to be partially or completely open at the level of the cell membrane. They can represent vesicles of the endoplasmic reticulum establishing contact with the cell surface, or small invaginations of the cell membrane forming cytoplasmic vacuoles or vesicles.

An earlier illustration (Figure 2) shows the vesicular bodies in question. Under Palade's first interpretation, the cisternae formed by elements of the endoplasmic reticulum might perhaps contain extracellular fluid, in which case the surface area available for transport could be substantially increased. At the same time, the membraneous or vesicular material obtained from cell homogenates might then be functionally and structurally akin to the plasma membrane, even if it originates largely from the reticulum.

This interpretation, however, is by no means a secure one. Serial sectioning has failed to bear out the proposed continuity of deep infoldings with the plasma membrane (cf. Andersson-Cedergren, 1959). The view that tubules filled with extracellular fluid penetrate deeply into the cell does not appear to have general support among cytologists. Nevertheless, analogous structure and transport behavior by these membranes is not ruled out.

Bacterial cells, being smaller, yield much higher proportions of membrane, for example, about 10 per cent. But such preparations include a large fraction of the catalytic machinery of the cell, which means that a much wider range of binding sites than those involved in transport from the environment must be exposed when such membranes are isolated. Apparently a very compact organization is characteristic of bacteria, so that much of the cell machinery is isolated with the membrane. Therefore, the natural accessibility of transport sites on unmodified cells probably presents such sites in higher purity than can be readily procured after tearing the membrane from the cell.

The isolation of red blood cell *ghosts* (Figure 25) may represent an interesting purification of membrane material. The erythrocyte can be lysed with water so that its hemoglobin (and other dissolved internal constituents) is distributed throughout the lysate. If electrolyte solutions are then added to restore isotonicity, the membrane gradually regains its integrity, selective permeability, and transport behavior, leaving most of the hemoglobin and other cytoplasmic components outside (Ponder, 1948; Székely et al., 1952; Teorell, 1952; Stein, 1956). Glucose entry is again mediated (Le-Fevre, 1961c), and in the presence of suitable energy sources, potassium ion may again be concentrated (Straub, 1954; Gardos, 1954; Hoffman, 1958). Perhaps the reversible hemolysis of the red blood cells supports the presence of pores in the plasma membrane, which may be enlarged by stretching that membrane.

How valuable the isolation of cell ghosts may be to the isolation and identification of the transport mediator remains to be seen. The technique has disposed of the view that potassium accumulation

73

**Figure 25** Human red blood cell ghost treated with phosphotungstic acid. Air-dried; shadowed. Magnification ×75,000. [*From Hillier, J., and Hoffman, J. F. (1953), J. Cell. Comp. Physiol., 42, 203; with permission.*]

can be explained by binding of potassium ion by hemoglobin or other dissolved cytoplasmic constituents. It has also permitted introduction of otherwise nonpenetrating solutes inside the cell; for example, Gardos (1954) showed that ATP introduced during the intermediate porous stage could actuate subsequent potassium uptake for several hours.

Glynn (1957a) has provided an extensive review of the composition and properties of the red blood cell membrane, undoubtedly the most satisfactory plasma membrane preparation available.

Model membranes, artificially produced from lipid or lipid and protein components, have so far been more useful for understanding the barrier action than the transport behavior of natural membranes. Mueller and his associates (1962) indicate, in a preliminary note, that they have prepared bimolecular membranes from the lipid and proteolipid of the white matter of brain. These membranes have very high electric resistance, but macromolecules adsorbed from the aqueous solutions separated by the membranes may greatly lower the resistance. An unidentified adsorbed macromolecule may cause the membranes to respond to an applied potential difference by a quickly reversible resistance change, a phenomenon seen with various natural membranes and undoubtedly relevant to the passage of charged particles. The authors suggest that they have reconstituted a cell membrane structure.

# 6

~~~~~~~~~~~~~~~

# Clues from
# associated events

## Persisting evidence of transient binding

In transport, as we have defined it throughout these discussions, the same apparently unchanged molecule that disappeared from phase 1 reappears in phase 2. Yet we must believe that this molecule has entered into a chemical reaction with a site of limited capacity, to account for the susceptibility of the migration to saturation or to inhibition by analogs. Many of the interactions that have been considered for transport might be expected to replace an atom of the transported solute with an identical (or an isotopic) atom from the environment. For example, if an amino acid forms an adenylic acid anhydride, in the instances studied, cleavage of this anhydride leaves the oxygen that was originally part of the carboxyl group of the amino acid, in the adenylic acid molecule, and a new oxygen is received by the amino acid from the environment (Hoagland et al., 1957). If the cleavage occurs in this characteristic way in transport, $O^{18}$ initially present in the amino acid should be displaced by $O^{16}$. The finding that very little $O^{18}$ loss occurred during the transport of $\alpha$-aminoisobutyric acid (Christensen et al., 1958) raises great doubt that an AMP anhydride arises as an intermediate. Binding of the carboxyl group of the amino acid in a peptide link or as a thio ester is, at the same time, apparently excluded.

Previously we have encountered also the observation that the oxygen at C2 of monosaccharides is not displaced during their intestinal transport, even though oxygen must be present at this position for mediation to occur. The remarkable fact is that not one case has been found of the persistence of an essential mark on a transported molecule to serve as a clue to the nature of the transport intermediate. This fact may well mean that binding to the transport site involves only displacement of atoms already so rapidly exchanged with the environment that we cannot expect to detect any acceleration of exchange. Hydrogen bonding and electrovalences may play a large part in the bonding of solutes to their transport sites. The peculiar flexibility in the structural requirement for sugar transport suggests somewhat indiscriminate hydrogen bonding to several of the hydroxyl groups (cf. Rosenberg, 1961). The probability that coenzymes or other small transferable groups act as transport carriers appears to be minimized by the absence of the predicted atom exchanges.

Clues to the character of the intermediation needed for transport may also come from incidental fates of a transported solute. If the solute is activated in a particular way, it may incidentally become more likely to form certain derivatives. The formation of N-acyl derivatives, perhaps peptides (Gale and Van Halteren, 1952), during amino acid transport, even if it occurs only in some organisms, might be a clue indicating that activation at the amino group occurs in the transport. This result might indicate, for example, that an N-phosphoryl derivative is formed. A hazard to be avoided is that an activation quite irrelevant to transport may occur; here again the use of transportable solutes escaping one or another enzymatic activation has helped to avoid erroneous conclusions.

An interesting case illustrating the isolation of a derivative formed incidentally to transport has been reported by Zabin and associates (1959; 1962). Isopropylthiogalactoside had previously been shown to be converted partially to the 6-O-acetyl derivative by Herzenberg, a result not published by him until 1961. Zabin and associates (1959) report that this acetylation is catalyzed by extracts of E. coli strains that have the specific galactoside transport system, but only to a small extent by the strains that lack the transport system. The acetyl derivative has been shown, however, not to be a possible intermediate in the transport. Its formation may nevertheless represent a clue to the nature of the intermediation.

77

If we could succeed in identifying a characteristic mark left by transport on a molecule, we could detect a catalytic action of the transport site in broken-cell preparations and perhaps monitor the isolation of the mediating structure.

## Associated physical fluxes

So far, transport has not yielded many of its chemical secrets. Despite many efforts to detect such a substance, no compound is recognized that shows anywhere near as large a preference for either sodium or potassium ion as is required to explain the biological discrimination. The failure of any of the procedures discussed so far to identify a single carrier or reactive site for the transport of any solute has stimulated investigators to try even more indirect approaches. One of these approaches seeks to observe whether another substance moves into or out of cells more rapidly whenever a transport is caused to occur. Such a behavior might have one of several meanings.

First, unless the carrier is strictly confined to the membrane phase, one might anticipate that rapid net transport would produce or accelerate an uptake of the carrier (or of one of its precursors) at least slightly at the receptor face of the membrane, or accelerate the release of it at the donor side of the membrane. This acceleration could be far less than stoichiometric to the flux of the solute under consideration. Detection of such an acceleration requires that the background flux of the carrier-related molecule be not too large. For example, a tetracoordinate metal ion could serve to join two amino acid molecules together (or a hexacoordinate metal, three amino acid molecules) so as to mask their polar properties and permit passage of a barrier. If so, one might anticipate an accelerated flux of the particular metal ion involved. An acceleration of $Mn(II)$ uptake by Ehrlich cells, but not of $Cu(II)$, $Zn(II)$, or $Fe(III)$, has been observed in association with increased amino acid loads (Pal and Christensen, 1959). Of course, the amino acids might serve in such experiments as metal-ion carriers, rather than the metal as an amino acid carrier, particularly considering that the basic amino acids are more conspicuously active in stimulating manganese uptake.

A second possible relationship may cause two fluxes to tend to occur together, a possibility we shall illustrate with the alkali metal fluxes associated with the movements of the amino acids and sugars. Ehrlich cells lose potassium ion and gain sodium ion as neutral amino acids are accumulated (Christensen and Riggs, 1952). This exchange appears to be meaningless as far as the preservation of electroneutrality is concerned, and should not be confused with migration of inorganic ions necessarily set up when cationic or anionic amino acids are transported (e.g., potassium ion uptake with glutamate). The ability of the Ehrlich cell to accumulate neutral amino acids has, in fact, been associated with their potassium-ion content, or their ability to receive sodium ion in exchange for it (Riggs et al., 1958). These alkali metal ion fluxes occurring when amino acids are taken up are large enough to suggest that one or both of them might supply the energy for the amino acid uptake, i.e., by driving the carrier outward to make it more available for amino acid entry. This suggestion might imply that energy is supplied directly to alkali metal transport only, other transports then being satellite transports. It is also significant that high sensitivity to alkali metal distribution, both for amino acid and sugar transport, is not found in human red blood cells but only where the transports are uphill. The evaluation by Hempling and Hare (1961) of the flux augmentation on adding glycine, however, leaves the energy available from the extra potassium-ion efflux alone somewhat short of that presumably required for glycine uptake. If we may also count the energy of the accompanying sodium-ion entry, to drive an amino acid carrier-complex inward, enough energy is available for the task. A perhaps more likely explanation will be suggested later in this chapter.

Similar associations of sodium-ion migration with the intestinal absorption of sugars and amino acids have also been observed and have received an interpretation somewhat similar to that given above (Csaky and Thale, 1960; Csaky, 1961; Crane et al., 1961). In this connection Csaky and associates (1961) and Crane and co-workers (1961) have observed that ouabain, known as an inhibitor of alkali metal transport, inhibits intestinal monosaccharide transport.

The dimerizer theory of Stein (1961a) makes one molecule of a solute the carrier for a second molecule. In this case, the kinetics will be expected to show the increase of influx (well below saturation) with the *square* of the solute concentration. In this connection, Luzzatto and Leoncini (1961) have observed higher-order kinetics for the cellular uptake of some sugars.

Stein has considered cases where two dissimilar sugars may dimerize and enter the cell together more readily than one of the sugars does alone (1961b). In this event, we should expect to see the influx of one sugar increased by the addition of the other. Accelerations of influx of one solute on the addition of an analogous solute have indeed been reported (Kepes, 1960; Jacques, 1961). These may also be produced by a stimulation of exchange. Stein (1961b) has also considered the situation in which the proposed mixed complex of two sugars is unsuitable to transport, but each of the "pure" dimers is suitable.

## Associated chemical fluxes

Although secondary physical migrations might be expected to present more characteristic clues to the nature of transport, acceleration of chemical reactions may also point to the identity of a carrier. Hokin and Hokin (1958; 1959a; 1959b) have observed that $P^{32}$ enters phosphatidic acids and certain other phospholipids more rapidly in a number of tissues when secretion is stimulated. The salt glands of the albatross or of the goose, which secrete hypertonic NaCl solutions, have been useful in this exploration. The Hokins have proposed a cycle of alkali metal transport whereby sodium ion leaves the cell through the lipid barrier as sodium phosphatidate. Phosphatidic acid is taken to be generated by action of ATP at the inside face of the membrane and is split by the action of a phosphatase to release the sodium ion from the outside face. This cleavage leaves phosphate as the not-too-plausible candidate for the role of carrier for potassium-ion uptake. Phosphatidate was chosen as sodium-ion carrier and phosphate as potassium-ion carrier because the phosphatidate-synthesizing system lies inside the cell, and not because of demonstrated differences in their affinity for the alkali metals. More recently the Hokins (1962) have entertained the hypothesis that the phosphatidic acid whose cleavage is associated with sodium-ion transport is part of a lipoprotein; the tertiary structure and alkali metal-binding properties of this lipoprotein may undergo a critical oscillative change when the phosphoester bond is split and reformed. Whatever the validity of either of these transport cycles, the association between the transport of hydrophilic solutes, on the one hand, and phosphatidate turnover, on the other, is an extremely interesting one. A nonmitochondrial phosphoprotein of liver slices shows a phosphorus turnover sensitive to the presence of sodium ion and of strophanthin (Ahmed and Judah, 1962).

Another important association of alkali metal transport with a chemical event is the correlation with an ATPase activity, developed by Dunham and Glynn, by Skou, and by Post and his associates. Skou (1957; 1960) discovered an ATPase of crab nerve that is particularly sensitive to $Na^+$ and $Mg^{++}$. Dunham (1957) observed that $10^{-6}$ $M$ strophanthidin diminished strongly the cleavage of ATP in the red blood cell, in association with an inhibition of potassium-ion influx (Schatzmann, 1953). Glynn (1957b) showed that scillarin A at very low levels acts as a competitive inhibitor of potassium-ion entry. Post observed that red blood cell stroma reached its maximal ATPase activity only when the sodium and potassium were set at certain concentrations. When both ions were set at ion levels permitting half-maximal alkali metal transport, the ATPase activity also became half-maximal. Ouabain produces a half-maximal inhibition of the ATPase at $10^{-7}$ $M$, also a half-maximal inhibition of cation transport (Post, 1959; Dunham and Glynn, 1960). This enzymatic ATP-splitting activity is associated with portions of the stroma that are not solubilized by deoxycholate (Post et al., 1960).

These experiments appear to identify the ATPase activity with the alkali metal transport process. The uphill transport of a number of solutes other than the alkali metal ions is also inhibited by very low levels of the cardiac glycosides and their derivatives. These include monosaccharides (Csaky et al., 1961), halide ions (Wolff and Maurey, 1958), and serotonin (Weissbach et al., 1960). Such results suggest that the relationship of ATPase action to uphill transport may be general.

Experiments by Caldwell (1959; 1960) and Caldwell and associates (1960) have, in the meantime, provided what is perhaps decisive evidence that high-energy phosphate compounds (perhaps ATP specifically) are the carriers of energy from the mitochondrion to the alkali metal transport apparatus.

These investigators injected ATP and other high-energy phosphorus compounds into the squid axon by use of a fine cannula inserted along the middle of the fiber. A section of axon had first been labeled with ionic $Na^{22}$ and then poisoned with cyanide; in this

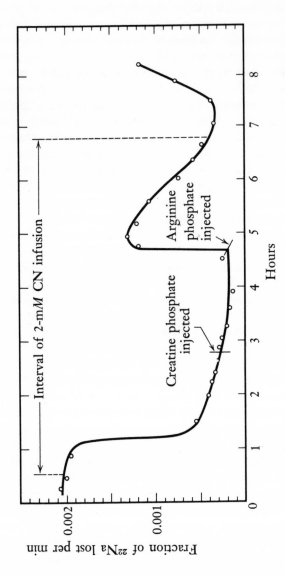

**Figure 26** The effect of injecting each of two high-energy phosphate compounds on sodium efflux from a cyanide-poisoned squid axon. Mean concentrations of 15.3-m*M* creatine phosphate and 15.8-m*M* arginine phosphate were present immediately after their injection. Temperature 19°C. [*From Caldwell, P. C. et al.* (1960), *J. Physiol.* (*London*), 152, 566; *with permission.*]

way the sodium-ion efflux was largely eliminated. The cyanide infusion rapidly depleted the levels of ATP and arginine phosphate. Subsequent infusion of either ATP or arginine phosphate, or of phosphoenolpyruvate or ADP, restored the sodium-ion efflux. Creatine phosphate was without effect, presumably because this animal species has no suitable kinase (Figure 26). ATP or arginine phosphate were ineffective when applied to the exterior of the axon. The action of these infusions was transient and could be demonstrated repeatedly at hourly intervals. The associations between the fluxes of alkali metal ions and the flux of sugars and amino acids, plus the mutual dependence of these transports on either respiration or glycolysis, leads to the view that high-energy phosphate also energizes these transports. At the same time, considerations of the energy expenditure for amino acid transport make it unlikely that ATP cleavage is linked *directly* to the transfer of the amino acid molecule (Heinz and Patlak, 1960).

In a preliminary note, Järnefelt (1961) reports that a microsomal preparation from brain fixes four or five times as much sodium ion if ATP is added. The report does not permit a conclusion as to whether this uptake by the organelle is a passive penetration, or a binding, or what. Tosteson (1960) has shown that the genetically potassium-low red blood cells of certain strains of sheep are relatively low in such ATPase activity, compared with homologous potassium-high erythrocytes.

If ATP serves as the energy source for transport, the total transport machinery must *a priori* appear as an ATP-splitting process. We should not suppose that a single, simple ATP-splitting enzyme molecule accomplishes alkali metal transport. Urea synthesis or muscle contraction may present a useful analogy to remind us of the complexity that we may expect to find where an ATP-splitting system performs work. The ATPase activity could for example represent the sum of the kinase and the phosphatase required by Hokins' phosphatidic acid cycle; or it could be considerably more complex.

Although transport has a vectorial component, we have seen earlier in this presentation that the energy may or may not actually serve to propel the solute physically against the concentration gradient; several of the published schemes propose that the physical migration in a final analysis occurs by diffusion. If, however, transport is produced by the application of a translocational force of a

83

relaxing macromolecular structure triggered by an entering solute, we could suppose that ATP in some way introduces the initial strained conformation.

Mitochondria are known to take up water and swell under certain conditions if respiration can occur simultaneously and to contract when ATP and magnesium ion are added (cf. Lehninger, 1960a; 1960b). Raaflaub (1953) suggested that enzymatically active, dilatable proteins might account for these morphologic changes. Lehninger (1959) used the term *mechanoenzymes* in extensions of this concept. He found that ATP cleavage occurs during the ATP-induced contraction and ceases when the contraction is maximal. A protein complex with suitable mechanical properties may serve to transduce the bond energy of ATP via mechanical energy into osmotic energy, at the same time acting as an ATPase; such a system may well function more widely by also acting in oxidative phosphorylation to receive energy from electron transport, converting it into the energy of a pyrophosphate bond in ATP via the potential energy inherent in strained protein structure.

Lehninger and Neubert (1961) have recently shown that a number of disulfide hormones that modify water and solute transport into and across cells also act on the mitochondrion, presumably in both cases by a disulfide-sulfhydryl exchange, to stimulate a respiration-dependent uptake of water (see Chapter 8). This behavior tends to show that water transport by the mitochondrion is closely related to transport by the plasma membrane. These authors do not suppose that the hormones produce their physiological effects by acting on the mitochondrion, but that inherent similarities in the various membranes of the cell permit this membrane to be taken as a model. Alkali metal transport into isolated nuclei and the dependence of their amino acid transport on sodium ion (Allfrey *et al.*, 1961) may also indicate similarities of this membrane to the plasma membrane.

Mitchell (1960b; 1961a; 1961b; 1961c) has proposed a model in which electron transport is taken to be linked to oxidative phosphorylation, the latter occurring as a translocation of $OH^-$ from the phosphate ion, so that the latter may add spontaneously to ADP. He has presented (1961c) his views in part as follows:

> According to the chemiosmotic hypothesis [Mitchell, 1960b; 1961a; 1961b], there are three main components of the organelles that catalyse oxidative phosphorylation: an oxido-reduction sys-

tem catalysing electron translocation; an adenosine triphosphatase system catalysing a reversible translocation of OH$^-$ ions
from inorganic phosphate; and a charge-impermeable membrane in which the oxido-reduction and adenosine triphosphatase
systems are orientated in opposition, so that the movement of
electrons across the membrane during oxido-reduction must push
a corresponding number of OH$^-$ ions from inorganic phosphate,
thus generating phosphorylium for donation to adenosine diphosphate. If this hypothesis were correct, one might reasonably suppose that uncouplers of oxidative phosphorylation could act by
making the membrane permeable to charge.

It has been discovered, by means of a simple titration technique, that the normally very low rate at which protons diffuse
through the membranes of washed suspensions of *Micrococcus
lysodeikticus* (Gilby and Few, 1958) and of rat-liver mitochondria isolated as described by Myers and Slater (1957) is increased manyfold by the addition of dicoumarol, 2,4-dinitro-
phenoxide, azide, and other uncouplers of oxidative phosphorylation. At low concentration of uncouplers of the dinitrophenol
type, the rate of conduction of protons across the membrane
is proportional to the amount of uncoupler added. The concentrations of the agents which give nearly complete uncoupling
(e.g., for the mitochondria: 20 $\mu$M-discoumarol; 100 $\mu$M-dinitro-
phenoxide; 2 m$M$-azide; for the bacteria: 10 times the concentrations of the same agents) have been found to catalyse the
passage of protons through the membranes of resting mitochondria or bacteria at rates equivalent to the rates of passage of
the electrons through the respective oxido-reduction systems
during uncoupled glutamate oxidation.

These observations are entirely consistent with the chemiosmotic coupling hypothesis which they were designed to test.
They also imply that the dinitrophenol type of uncoupling agent
owes its activity to two factors (a) solubility in a nonpolar region in the membrane of the phosphorylation system (Shaw,
Lannon and Tapley, 1959), and (b) the capacity for conducting
protons across this region. The latter capacity can possibly be
ascribed most simply to the presence of two or more alternative
weakly acidic groups between which the proton-bonding electron can pass by way of the $\pi$-orbitals present in all uncouplers
of this type.

He also wrote (1961b):

> In the exact sciences, cause and effect are no more than events
> linked in sequence. Biochemists now generally accept the idea
> that metabolism is the cause of membrane transport. The under-
> lying thesis of the hypothesis put forward here is that if the
> processes that we call metabolism and transport represent events

in a sequence, not only can metabolism be the cause of transport, but also transport can be the cause of metabolism. Thus, we might be inclined to recognize that transport and metabolism, as usually understood by biochemists, may be conceived advantageously as different aspects of one and the same process of vectorial metabolism.

In this hypothesis (Figure 27) the process of oxidative phosphorylation is seen as a transport, which may be linked to electron transport but which, presumably, may equally well be linked to a specific molecular transport, functioning instead as an ATP-splitting system.

Mitchell's hypothesis offers us a third possibility, beyond those presented in the second and third paragraphs of this chapter, for interpreting flux associations such as those seen between amino acids and the alkali metal ions. Uphill transports may well not be placed *in series*, e.g., with alkali metal transport driving amino acid transport; but *in parallel*, with many or all uphill transports driven by the response of membrane structure to ATP cleavage. The mainte-

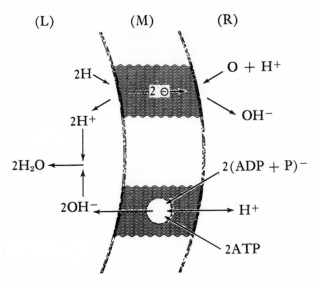

**Figure 27** Mitchell's scheme for linkage of electron-transport system to oxidative phosphorylation, the latter produced by a reversible ATPase system. See text for discussion. [*From Mitchell, P.* (1961), *Nature,* **191,** 144; *with permission.*]

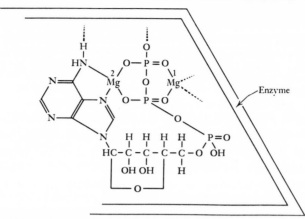

**Figure 28** Hypothetical scheme for relationship between enzyme, ATP, and magnesium ions. Such a positioning of magnesium-ATP on the membrane is proposed by Skou to permit it to displace electrons within the membrane. [*From Skou, J. C.* (1960), *Biochim. et Biophys. Acta,* **42**, 19; *with permission.*]

nance of an activated, transport-responsive state of the membrane may then be aided by the presence of high cellular levels of potassium ion or of amino acids, or of both.

We may note that Mitchell's scheme included an electron-transport system possessing direction across a membrane, of the type originally proposed by Lundegaardh (1939) as the basis of anion transport. The idea that material transport is produced by this system (see the writings of Conway and of Davies), without the associated participation of a similarly anisotropic ATPase system, is not, however, being reintroduced in this hypothesis. Mitchell's proposal appears to make from the two perhaps most perplexing problems of biology—solute transport and oxidative phosphorylation —a single problem.

Skou (1961) speculates that ATP acts on alkali metal transport by being bound to the membrane by the aromatic amino group and through the intermediation of a magnesium ion (Figure 28). A second magnesium ion may occupy a position to make one common electronic system of the phosphate chain and the adenine part of the ATP, with common nonlocalized electrons (Szent-Györgyi, 1957; 1960). The linkage to the membrane may then conceivably permit ATP to influence (and perhaps also to respond to) the distribution of electrons within the membrane. This movement of electrons is visualized as taking place across a series of fixed molecular sites extending through the membrane. These are taken to be anionic sites able to bind the alkali metal ions. The theory of Eisenman, Rudin, and Casby (see Eisenman, 1961, for references) is used to account for the corresponding movement of a differential affinity for the sodium and potassium ions. According to this theory, an increase in the negative field strength of a chemical grouping can cause its affinity for sodium ion to exceed that for potassium ion. Inversely, a decrease in the negative electrostatic field strength can favor potassium-ion binding.

The joining of ATP is supposed to initiate an electron migration away from the most remote alkali metal-binding site to a dis-

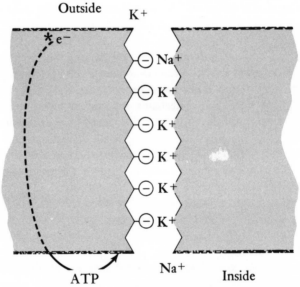

**Figure 29** Visualization adapted from Skou (1961) of $Na^+$ extrusion in exchange for $K^+$ across a series of points whose relative affinity for $Na^+$ and $K^+$ is made to change sequentially by the migration of an electron. The arc marked ATP illustrates the hypothetical position of bound $Mg_2ATP$ (as in Figure 28) and the direction of the electron movement it induces. See text for discussion.

tinct electron donor-acceptor nearby, and thence across the membrane by an unspecified route to the P-O-P structure of ATP (see Figure 29). A cleavage of the pyrophosphate bond then donates the electron to the nearest of the series of alkali metal-binding sites, causing it to exchange its potassium ion for a sodium ion from the interior of the cell. The electron is thereby permitted to move to the next deeper site, causing the new sodium ion to progress to this site in exchange for a potassium ion already there. In this way, the selective affinity for sodium ion progresses through the membrane to the most remote binding site, from which the sodium ion is exchanged for a potassium ion; the potassium ion comes from the exterior as the electron is transferred to the nearby electron acceptor, under the attractive action of a new ATP binding to the initial site.

In this scheme no movement of a carrier occurs; instead only the specific affinity moves as an electron migrates through the system. No mode of linkage whereby ATP breakdown could cause sugars or amino acids to migrate across a series of fixed points is inherent in the proposal. A demonstration of the affinity change with electron movement in model structures would provide material support for this proposal.

One is tempted to consider whether a system of this kind could not also produce ATP synthesis in the mitochondrion, provided that a sufficient potential difference exists between a participating electron donor and a different electron acceptor.

# 7

~~~~~~~~~~~~~~~~~~~~~~~~~~~~~~

# *Nutritional and genetic approaches*

## Nutritional approaches

We may illustrate the nutritional approach by reviewing the observations of the effect of deficiency of vitamin $B_6$ on amino acid transport. Ehrlich ascites tumor cells grown in $B_6$-deficient mice are subnormal in accumulating glycine at high loads; added pyridoxal stimulates such deficient cells more strongly than it does ordinary Ehrlich cells (Christensen *et al.*, 1954). The model amino acid, $\alpha$-aminoisobutyric acid, is concentrated much more weakly by many tissues (except liver) of the intact $B_6$-deficient rat than by tissues of well-nourished rats (Riggs and Walker, 1958). Rats receiving 4-deoxypyridoxine (Jacobs and Hillman, 1958; 1960) or penicillamine (Akedo *et al.*, 1960) show deficient intestinal transport of amino acids, corrected by pyridoxal phosphate supplementation. Adding the coenzyme to the perfused intestine eliminates the inhibiting action of 2,4-dinitrophenol on amino acid transport (Ueda *et al.*, 1960).

These observations have been particularly interesting because pyridoxal, or its phosphate, is able to take hold of amino acids by Schiff-base formation at the amino group, in a manner that could perhaps satisfy the requirements for the behavior of the carrier or the transport site. Somewhat against this view stands the high resistance of amino acid transport in the Ehrlich ascites tumor cell to inhibition by carbonyl reagents such as semicarbazide, hydroxylamine, and aminoxyacetic acid (Christensen, 1960b). At the same time, the stimulating action of the addition of $10^{-3}$ to $10^{-4}$ $M$ pyridoxal or pyridoxal phosphate on amino acid transport by the Ehrlich cell does not seem likely to represent merely an augmentation of a suboptimal carrier level (Pal and Christensen, 1961). Furthermore, these agents seem to slow exodus more than they accelerate entry of amino acids (Oxender, 1962b).

Even though the action of pyridoxal at millimolar levels on amino acid transport into Ehrlich cells does not represent a physiological action, the nutritional experiments cited above show that vitamin $B_6$ is somehow related to amino acid transport.

## Genetic approaches

If any organism, mutant or otherwise, requires that a specific carrier precursor be supplied from the environment, a special opportunity for identifying the carrier is presented.

A number of genetic deficiencies of transport, especially of renal transport, are known. Cystinuria has been known for a century and a half. Amino acids other than cystine, including lysine (Ackermann and Kutscher, 1912), were occasionally observed to be excreted along with cystine. Cadaverine and putrescine were also detected; these diamines may have arisen from lysine and ornithine by bacterial action during the collection of urine. Full recognition, however, of cystinuria as a genetically determined disease of transport involving lysine, arginine, cystine, and ornithine is comparatively recent (Dent, 1949; Dent and Rose, 1951; Stein, 1951; Dent et al., 1954). Although cystine is indeed a diamino acid, so far it has not been shown in any well-defined system to use the same transport mediator as the cationic amino acids (cf. Rosenberg et al., 1962).

In 1937 Kerr recognized "a different race" of sheep having high red blood cell potassium levels in contrast to the majority of sheep, which have low erythrocyte levels of this ion, with correspondingly high sodium-ion levels. Evans (1954) showed that the same division into two strains occurs in English and Scottish sheep; Evans and King (1955) showed that the high-potassium character was inherited in a simple Mendelian manner. The potentialities inherent in such genetically determined transport deficiencies may be illustrated by the finding that the erythrocyte potassium level of these two strains can be correlated with their ATPase level (Tosteson et al., 1960).

Gale demonstrated and studied from 1947 to 1955 (cf. 1953) the wide occurrence of amino acid transport processes in bacteria. Doudoroff discussed in 1951 the problem of bacterial mutants able to use a given disaccharide but not one of its component sugars despite the presence of appropriate enzymes. He emphasized the possibility that the absence of specific enzymes necessary for permeation might exclude certain monosaccharides from the cell interior.

Lag periods in the utilization of particular organic substrates have frequently been encountered by microbiologists, and between 1951 and 1955 one often finds such comments as these: "Apparently . . . the period of adaptation with the resting cells was the time necessary for elaboration of the system necessary for transferring the substrates across the membrane" (Stone and Wilson, 1952); "It may be that some type of transport or carrier system is being synthesized . . . [during the lag period]" (Barrett et al., 1953); "On this hypothesis the adaptive process would consist of the formation of the particular enzyme necessary for the movement of the substrate" (Kogut and Podoski, 1953).

In 1955 Cohen and Rickenburg (cf. Monod, 1956) brought vigorous new attention to such genetic transport differences in microorganisms, especially with regard to β-thiogalactoside transport in E. coli. Their results showed that inducible transports could probably operate uphill and that they are, in general, not different from other known carrier transports (Cohen and Monod, 1957). Nevertheless a new name *permease* was recommended for transport processes, or for the inducible part of such processes, or for an enzymatic part. This term has been critically received (see Appendix 1 for discussion), and it will be avoided here because it seems to produce an unproductive compartmentalization of communication.

This comment concerns the unfortunate term *permease* only. The important potentialities inherent in the absence of a particular transport process in mutants are already evident. For example, if mutants that are unable to transport alkali metal can be identified (cf. Schultz and Solomon, 1961), very important comparisons with wild-type strains should be possible. We trust, however, that if the mode of alkali metal transport is first described in bacteria it will not be called a *permease*, unless we should at that time be ready to speak also of the *potassium-ion permease* of red blood cells.

# Endocrinology of transport

## General

We may assume that long before the ductless glands appeared, enzymes and metabolic sequences and cycles were evolved in the interlocking patterns in simple organisms. As the design of the complex multicellular organism was approached, specific agencies acting on certain cells and controlling certain processes had then to be superimposed. Basically, the cells of these organisms have essentially similar metabolic processes. An obvious means of differentiation lay in developing somewhat different transport relationships to their environment; a means of developing mutual controls lay in developing receptor sites on the surfaces of certain cells, where the fixation of humoral agents could accentuate or inhibit transport processes by which particular solutes gain access to those cells. The difference in the readiness with which sugars gain access to the hepatic cell and to the muscle cell is as remarkable as the difference in their responsiveness to insulin.

Instead, biochemists have generally been optimistic that the "targets" of hormone action would eventually be identified as enzymes and enzymatic reactions. Although a number of hormone effects on enzymatic reactions have been observed, these have only in a very few cases corresponded at all well with the physiologic action of the hormone. In the case of a number of hormones, direct actions on enzymes are still unknown. In the meantime, a number of powerful actions on transport, without the obvious mediation of separate enzyme systems, have come to be recognized, and the conception has gained strength that endocrinologic effects may frequently concern barriers and access.

Rudolph Peters has voiced a related idea, that hormones act on the "cytoskeleton" of the cell (1956). He suggests that a hormone may, by entering the surface of the cell, change anatomic orientations not only in the plasma membrane but in other structural elements throughout the cell so that several enzymatic reactions are modified simultaneously. Hechter and Lester (1960) have voiced similar views.

The present discussion, which continues earlier comment from this laboratory (Christensen, 1948, see also Appendix 2; Noall et al., 1957), summarizes the instances in which hormones appear to modify transport processes.

## Aldosterone

Of the several steroids that modify alkali metal transport, aldosterone is outstanding in its potency, particularly on the renal tubule. It has so distinct an action to intensify the exchange of sodium ion from the fluid passing through the lumen, for potassium ion from the plasma, that the behavior may serve as a sensitive assay for the hormone. At the same time, the distribution of the alkali metal ions between the cells and the extracellular fluid is recognized to be disturbed in adrenal cortical deficiency, and to be modified by mineralcorticoid therapy. Aldosterone has also been found to modify sodium-ion transport by the frog skin, by the salivary gland, and by the sweat glands.

## Estrogens

In 1957 Noall and associates showed that the administration of a microgram of $\beta$-estradiol to the weanling female rat caused a tripling of the level of $\alpha$-aminoisobutyric acid in the uterus, this model amino acid having been permitted in advance to distribute itself throughout the animal. Noall and Allen (1961) later showed that estradiol can intensify the accumulation of $\alpha$-aminoisobutyric acid by the uterus of the rabbit in a 30-minute interval. We may perhaps rationalize that such an action applied to ordinary amino acids permits this organ to accelerate its protein synthesis and

95

growth. A number of ordinary amino acids have their concentrations in the uterus approximately doubled in 24 hours but apparently not in 4 hours after estradiol is given, according to Kalman and Lombrozo (1961). Transports are often modified together by the same agency; in this case an acceleration of urea entry into the uterus has also been recorded recently (Kalman et al., 1961). Other uterine transport changes will probably also be found to be produced by estrogens.

The inhibition of hexose passage across the human red blood cell membrane by stilbestrol has already been discussed. The same agent, together with estradiol, estradiol disulfate, and stilbestrol disulfate, also inhibits phosphate entry into red cells (Christensen and Jones, 1961). Under special conditions, estradiol disulfate stimulates the mediated uptake of uric acid by these cells. The disulfates of estradiol and stilbestrol at 1-m$M$ levels stimulate amino acid accumulation by the Ehrlich cell (Christensen, 1960b). Other steroids are less active on the red blood cell membrane; e.g., rather high levels of corticosterone are required to inhibit fructose uptake (Pletscher et al., 1955). Estradiol also increases, and testosterone decreases, the renal excretion rate of the rat for the model amino acids, $\alpha$-aminoisobutyric and 1-aminocyclopentanecarboxylic acids (Riggs and Walker, 1962). These actions taken together imply widespread sensitivity of transports to steroids.

Physiologically significant hormone actions may perhaps occur only when the membrane has binding sites with sufficient affinity to fix a steroid present at the relatively low physiological levels; perhaps this site must also be appropriately close to the solute-transporting site.

## Glucocorticoids on hepatic amino acid uptake

Trauma or fever are known to lower the plasma amino acids. Laparotomy in rats was shown to produce this action, and at the same time to increase the hepatic concentrations of amino acids (Christensen et al., 1948). The injection of hydrocortisone (or, less effectively, of cortisone) quickly produces the same effect. For this purpose the model amino acid, $\alpha$-aminoisobutyric acid, was used to restrict other possible sources of the change in distribution (Noall et al., 1957; Christensen, 1960a; Kaplan and Nagareda, 1961). The suggestion has been made that (a) the catabolic effect of the glucocorticoids, (b) their gluconeogenic effect, and (c) their stimulation of plasma protein synthesis all arise from a stimulation of the hepatic capture of the normal amino acids (Noall *et al.*, 1957). This action would make the amino acids more accessible to a variety of hepatic processes.

Up to the present time, unfortunately, no really satisfactory preparation has been made available for studying transport into liver cells *in vitro*. The normal hepatic behavior seen in the intact animal toward both potassium ion and amino acids is easily lost on slicing the tissue, on preparation of free cells, or even on perfusion. In contrast, slices of certain other tissues, such as cerebral or renal cortex, have shown interesting transport behavior.

## Vasopressin

The renal control of the tonicity of the body fluids is assisted by the variable output of the antidiuretic hormone, vasopressin, from the posterior pituitary gland. This octapeptide is believed to decrease diuresis by facilitating the reabsorption of water, which moves under an osmotic gradient through the wall of the distal tubule from a hypotonic fluid in the lumen. This action may well differ from all the rest of those discussed in this section because of the relatively enormous number of molecules handled by the transporting system.

Fong and associates (1960) have obtained evidence that circulating vasopressin becomes fixed to the membrane of the tubular epithelium by a disulfide-exchange reaction, the permeability of the membrane to water being modified in this way. These investigators found that circulating tritium-labeled vasopressin became bound in the rat kidney in such a manner as to appear in a sedimented membraneous fraction, from which the tritium was partially released by the action of sulfhydryl compounds but not by electrodialysis. Furthermore, prior treatment of the toad bladder with thiol-blocking agents diminished subsequent fixation of tritium-labeled vasopressin (Schwartz *et al.*, 1960). Figure 30 shows a visualization by these authors of the disulfide-exchange process fixing vasopressin to the plasma membrane. Since the hormone apparently accelerates a *saturable* (and therefore mediated) entry of sodium ion into the cells of the toad bladder from the mucosal side (Frazier *et al.*, 1962), the diagram probably should not be interpreted as simply an opening of pores to molecular migration. The fact that vasopressin must be applied to the serosal (outer) surface of the toad bladder to

97

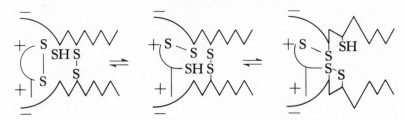

**Figure 30** Schematic representation of the hypothetical action of the antidiuretic hormone. Through electrostatic attractions or hydrogen bonding, the hormone is aligned at the receptor site. A thiol-disulfide exchange reaction follows. This triggers a chain reaction of sulfhydryl-disulfide reactions, which brings about conformational changes in the protein components of the diffusion barrier to permit increased flux of water and certain solutes. The hormone-receptor disulfide bond is ultimately cleaved enzymatically to restore the membrane to its original state. [*From Fong, C. T. O., et al.* (1960), *Proc. Natl. Acad. Sci. U.S.*, **46,** 1273; *with permission.*]

modify migration through the mucosal surface of the cells undoubtedly has implications for the mode of action.

An entirely different proposal as to the mode of action of vasopressin has been made by Orloff and associates (1962). These authors point out that, under suitable conditions of injection, the hormone can mimic the action of ACTH in causing hydrocortisone release from the adrenal cortex and can mimic the action of glucagon in causing glucose release from the liver (Hilton *et al.*, 1959; Bergen *et al.*, 1960). Orloff and his associates suggest that both actions are intermediated by adenosine-3′,5′ cyclic phosphate. This substance, they suggest, may be frequently involved in actions on membranes. The following scheme is proposed:

vasopressin          theophylline

$$\text{ATP} \longrightarrow \text{cyclic } 3',5'\text{-AMP} \longrightarrow 5'\text{-AMP}$$

permeability
change

Cyclic AMP was shown to stimulate water migration and sodium transport when it was applied at 1- to 10-m$M$ levels to the serosal surface of the toad bladder. Theophylline at a 40-m$M$ level also produced this action. The effects of a submaximal dose each of vasopressin and theophylline were additive. Each agent was ineffective when applied to the mucosal surface. The action of all three was blocked by 1-m$M$ N-ethylmaleimide and by $p$-chloromercuribenzoate. An actual increase in the level of the cyclic anhydride in toad bladder under the action of vasopressin has not yet been shown. This proposal has special interest in that it supplies possible transport-modifying actions for several more hormones.

## Insulin

Apparently as "a voice in the wilderness" urging attention to the importance of transport and its control, Rudolph Höber suggested in 1914, before insulin was known, that diabetes might well be a disease of sugar transport by the cell membrane (Levine, 1961). Lundsgaard showed in 1939 that insulin accelerated sugar uptake by perfused striated muscle. Levine and his associates showed, beginning in 1949 (see also Levine, 1961), that insulin accelerates the entry of sugars into the cellular compartment as estimated for the whole organism. This action has since been confirmed specifically for a number of isolated tissues, including particularly the heart, the diaphragm, and the epididymal fat pad. These tissues are believed not to concentrate sugars and may appear not to admit them to all the cellular space; nevertheless, the entry at least into muscle is mediated in the absence as well as in the presence of insulin. The diaphragm of the insulin-treated rat *in situ* appears to take up D-xylose to a level twice as high as the plasma level (Eichhorn and Hechter, 1961). The possibility that the outward transport can be uphill has received insufficient attention.

The isolated diaphragm takes up a number of amino acids faster when insulin is added. These amino acids include $\alpha$-amino-isobutyric acid (Kipnis and Noall, 1958), glycine (Manchester and Young, 1960; cf. Manchester, 1961), also L-methionine and L-proline, and a number of model amino acids (Akedo and Christensen, 1962b). A tentative impression that this action occurs only for abnormal amino acids is not correct. More probably the hormone acts on only one of two mediating systems (the so-called "A" mediator) for neutral amino acids discussed in Chapter 4.

99

The action by insulin on two entirely distinct transport processes (for sugars and for amino acids) deserves close attention. We should not infer, however, that a decompartmentalization has occurred, i.e., that barriers to diffusion have been removed, since these solutes do not move simply by diffusion. Instead the transports in question are mediated; the uptake of amino acids appears in most cases to be concentrative. For $\alpha$-aminoisobutyric acid, Akedo and Christensen (1962b) have shown that the diffusion constant is not modified by insulin, but that insulin influences instead a mediated process in such a way that the apparent $K_m$ is strongly decreased.

The finding by Barrnett and Ball (1960) that the frequency of invagination and pinocytosis of the cells of the epididymal fat pad, as estimated by electron microscopy (Figure 31), is increased by insulin, may be taken as another indication that the cell membrane has been affected in a general way, and not simply with reference to the mediation of sugar transport. We have already seen the difficulties in supposing that the extra sugar enters by the increased pinocytosis per se. More likely, the increased frequency of invagination reflects a modification of the membrane associated with an increased responsiveness to entering solutes. The transport of sodium and potassium ions is also known to be influenced by insulin (Manery et al., 1956; Smillie and Manery, 1960; Kernan, 1961). Note that steroids also modify a variety of apparently unrelated transports in other cells and tissues. It is striking how frequently hormones seem to act on a generalized transport property of the plasma membrane rather than on a single specific transport.

Randle (1956) has shown that glucose entry into muscle is also accelerated by the absence of oxygen or by the presence of 2,4-dinitrophenol, salicylate, or other agents (Randle and Smith, 1958). A common effect that can be attributed to these agencies is a decreased availability of high-energy phosphate. Hence Randle has suggested that insulin may act by diverting high-energy phosphate away from a presumed repressive effect on sugar transport. In apparent contrast, the action of dinitrophenol on $\alpha$-aminoisobutyric acid transport is inhibitory rather than insulin-like (Akedo and Christensen, 1962b). Such transport of $\alpha$-aminoisobutyric acid into the isolated diaphragm becomes uphill when insulin is added; being an uphill transport it presumably *requires* ATP and, as would be expected, is antagonized by 2,4-dinitrophenol. Under these conditions, the conclusion that insulin modifies transport by diverting

**Figure 31**  Electron micrograph of portions of the cytoplasm of two adjacent adipose cells which had been incubated in a bicarbonate medium containing glucose, gelatin, and insulin (4 mg, 2 mg, and $10^3$ microunits per ml, respectively). The arrows indicate what are described as numerous infoldings of the plasma membrane, as well as small vesicles. Magnification, ×37,000. [*From Barrnett, R. J., and Ball, E. G.* (1960), *J. Biophys. Biochem. Cytol.,* **8,** 91; *with permission.*]

ATP from an action on the plasma membrane represents an over-simplification.

N-Ethylmaleimide has been shown to interfere with the action of insulin on sugar transport and on the fixation of insulin by the perfused heart (Candenas *et al.*, 1961; cf. Pittman *et al.*, 1961; Fong *et al.*, 1962). Attention has been called to the necessity of the intact disulfide-bridged structure of insulin for its action on sugar transport, and to the degree of similarity of its intrachain disulfide bridge to that of vasopressin. Perhaps here also the hormone becomes fixed to the membrane by a disulfide exchange to modify its behavior as proposed previously for vasopressin.

Lehninger and Neubert (1961; Neubert and Lehninger, 1962) find that the mitochondrion is stimulated to take up water in the presence of vasopressin, oxytocin, or insulin, each at $10^{-4}$ to $10^{-5}$ $M$. This action resembles a much weaker one of oxidized glutathione. Furthermore, the action in all these cases is potentiated by the presence of reduced glutathione or certain other thiols. This water uptake depends on simultaneous respiration, and the water is re-extruded if ATP is added to the mitochondrial suspension. Melhuish and Greenbaum (1961) have shown that zinc insulin and the pituitary growth hormone (which contains four disulfide links) also cause mitochondrial swelling. Although no formal demonstration that these hormones bind by disulfide-sulfhydryl exchange is yet available, the association of these effects, on the one hand, with the action of simpler sulfur compounds and, on the other hand, with the action of these hormones on other transport systems, establishes a strong inference.

The hormone levels required to provoke mitochondrial swelling are high by biological standards. Lehninger and Neubert (1961) do not suppose that all the hormones known to stimulate mitochondrial swelling act physiologically in this way. Instead, they emphasize that the same type of sandwiched, stratified lipid-protein arrangement probably occurs in various cellular membranes, and hence the action on the mitochondrion may serve as a model for the action of the disulfide hormones on other membranes, including the plasma membrane. These results further the concept that many transports may find their common basis in the behavior of the protein structure of biological membranes, which is probably closely associated with the transfer of energy involved in the formation and breakdown of ATP (Christensen, 1960b; 1961; see closing paragraph of Chapter 4). The apparently multiple effects of insulin in modifying the formation and fate of ATP may easily have a common basis in a reversible action of membrane structures in the synthesis and breakdown of ATP.

## Thyroxine

The uncoupling action of this hormone on oxidative phosphorylation does not occur in disrupted mitochondria (Tapley et al., 1955; see Lehninger et al., 1958; Lehninger, 1960a). The intact mitochondrion is caused to swell by $10^{-8}$ $M$ thyroxine and by analogous chemical structures that increase the basal metabolic rate. Furthermore, mitochondria isolated from hyperthyroid rats show a much higher spontaneous swelling rate than those from normal animals, whereas mitochondria from hypothyroid rats are very resistant to swelling (Tapley, 1956). The physiologic action of this hormone remains, however, a subject of inquiry.

## Parathyroid hormone

Calcium has been shown to be concentrated from the mucosal to the serosal compartment of the everted rat small intestine (Schacter and Rosen, 1959). That a higher calcium-ion activity is indeed produced by this transport has been demonstrated using the frog heart, which is responsive only to ionized calcium. The degree of concentration achieved is greater when the rat had previously received parathyroid hormone (Rasmussen, 1959), but an effect of the hormone added directly to the in vitro preparation has not yet been observed.

## Pituitary growth hormone

Noall and associates (1957) showed that, in the intact rat, the steady-state level of α-aminoisobutyric acid in muscle and several other tissues, relative to the extracellular level, is increased by bovine growth hormone. Kostyo et al. (1959), and Kostyo and Engel (1960) demonstrated an accelerating action of the hormone on the entry of this model amino acid into the isolated rat diaphragm. A prompt acceleration by bovine growth hormone of the passage of an injected dose of α-aminoisobutyric acid from the plasma into the muscle of the rat was shown by Riggs and Walker (1960). These actions may play a part in the growth-promoting action of this hormone. A tendency for the muscle/plasma ratio of $\alpha$-amino-isobutyric acid to decrease with age has been seen in the rat (Riggs and Walker, 1958) and also in man (Christensen *et al.*, 1958).

## Adrenocorticotrophic hormone

Eichhorn and associates (1960) have shown that the entry of D-xylose into the adrenal cortex is accelerated under the influence of ACTH.

## General considerations

These numerous examples suggest that hormones very frequently act by modifying the access of metabolites to various cells through effects on transport processes. The simplicity of such a basis of superimposed control is obvious. The author (1960b; 1961) has felt that such widespread action of hormones on transport, often involving the simultaneous change of more than one specific transport, supports the concept that transport sites could arise from closely ordered relations between chemical groups in the matrix of the membrane and, further, that transport behavior may be occasioned by distortions and translocations of such ordered relations.

At the same time, the very properties by which hormones bind to the surface of cells may permit them also to bind to soluble enzymes, thereby modifying their catalytic action. Direct actions on soluble enzymes have generally not yet been demonstrated to occur in the intact animal treated with a dose of hormone within the physiological range. But a conclusion that all hormone effects are produced by actions on cell transport would obviously be quite unwarranted.

## Pharmacology of transport

Attention will be called only briefly to the great number and range of drugs that act on, or may be considered to act on, biological barriers and barrier activities. One could perhaps safely maintain that at this time more pharmacological effects are obtained by this route than by action on nonbarrier enzyme systems.

# 9

~~~~~~~~~~~~~~~~~~

# *General summary*

Cell function requires the presence of barriers. These barriers permit the passage of some molecules but not of others. Their selectivity does not arise entirely from the nature of the barrier material, but also from the presence of mediating groups to which molecules meeting certain structural and conformational requirements bind. As a consequence, these molecules may be released into the phase lying beyond the barrier, in some cases at a higher concentration than existed in the phase of origin. The energy causing this result may reach the membrane in the form of ATP, or it may conceivably be represented at least partially by an established gradient of another solute, possibly an analogous one. The system that accepts the energy from ATP may conceivably be the same system, a transport system, that generates ATP when electrons are transported.

The reactive sites that mediate transport can readily be detected in intact cells, but means for recognizing them in simpler systems are mainly lacking. Their modes of gripping the solute molecule do not seem to leave a permanent mark on the transported solute. The nature of transport specificity suggests that the several components of each site are distributed in a three-dimensional matrix, as if in a macromolecular structure; but the specificity patterns tend to differ from those of known enzymes. For such reasons, the proposed models from which we seek to explain uphill transport by changes in the shapes of molecules forming part of the barrier seem particularly attractive. The accessibility of transport processes to endocrine modification and the frequency with which such effects have been demonstrated *in vivo* appear further to support the participation by exposed structures of the plasma membrane.

Although most of the approaches to the understanding of transport have so far been indirect, direct chemical marking of the reactive structures, or other means of monitoring their presence during direct isolation procedures, appear to be a promising mode of attack. The main objective, the identification of the mediating structures and the demonstration of their action in isolation, remains before us.

## Speculation on the future course of transport research

I have been urged to add a word of speculation about the future. One can detect, I think, a rising excitement in the transport field, which we may perhaps interpret as an optimism that a molecular description of transport may be reached in the present generation. If true, this is a strange optimism when we recall that not a single binding structure engaged in transport has yet been identified, and that we have only indirect indications of where the answer is to be found.

Nevertheless, I believe that one may notice a disenchantment with the "stamp-collecting" stage of transport research; a decrease in the satisfaction arising from the description of yet one more mediated transfer showing the usual characteristics. Certainly investigators are placing on one another more sophisticated requirements for differentiating between transport and binding, between net migration and exchange, or between transport and other access processes. Furthermore, each new case of mediation tends to receive rather prompt evaluation with regard to any special advantage or fruitfulness that can be derived from it.

I think one may also detect that schemes and models embodying parts of the information gained by indirect means about a transport system produce only tentative satisfaction. The feeling is widespread, I believe, that definite molecular answers should be forthcoming.

How are the chemical structures producing transport then to be identified and isolated? First, let me indicate my high hopes that specific endgroup reagents may be discovered, such as those for the reactive sites of enzymes. These should serve to mark a given transport site and to monitor its isolation. Perhaps an amino acid analog can be constructed that will first bind as usual at the transport site, and then either spontaneously, or upon irradiation or other special treatment, bond itself stably to adjoining parts of the mediating structure. Means are then available through isotope labeling to intensify the specificity of such markers.

One must bear in mind that the molecules involved in transport mediation are probably insoluble and macromolecular. They are likely to be either embedded in or integral with the membrane structure. Therefore isolative procedures probably must solubilize the components, a procedure that may well destroy their function. Two lines of analytical effort can be foreseen: one to separate, without the necessity of preserving function, the stably marked mediating structure; the other to use the persistence of at least an aspect of transport behavior to guide the isolation of a component. Obviously, in the latter approach, a narrower range of procedures will be applicable. The preparation of artificial lipid or lipoprotein barriers, and the study of their transport properties, are other promising approaches.

A general exploration of the nature of the structure of the plasma membrane may uncover further technical means of separating components functioning in transport. For such exploration we should probably select membranes with minimal metabolic potentialities other than transport; for example, the red blood cell membrane is functionally much simpler than membrane preparations obtained so far from bacteria. In mutants lacking a given transport, attention will fall on the absence of any component possessed by the *wild* type.

Given that an uphill transport may represent in its totality an ATPase activity, we may be led to the mediating structure by following the course of the terminal phosphoryl residue of ATP up to the point where it finally appears as inorganic phosphate. For example, a membrane lipoprotein in which the contained diglyceride can be phosphorylated to yield a phosphatidic acid may prove to be a key component. No doubt such lipoproteins will be studied for their ability to bind specifically solutes undergoing uphill transport.

But if, instead, the cleavage of ATP is per se a vectorial event, as Mitchell suggests, occasioning the migration of hydroxyl ion across a barrier, the receptors of the resultant phosphoryl group may have only secondary significance, and the structures linking hydroxyl ion migration with the movement of other ions or molecules are apt not to be those receiving the phosphoryl group.

In any case, in this speculative section I venture the prediction that transport will be found to be produced by macromolecular structures in the matrix of the membrane, and not by small, free, shuttling carriers trapped in the membrane phase. The currently rather mystifying swelling and contracting of mitochondria that are apparently also sensitive to sulfhydryl-disulfide exchange, will, I suggest, prove to be a general manifestation of the behavior of cellular membranes. This behavior of membranes may prove to underlie many or all uphill transports and facilitated diffusions. It is also possible that our present understanding of macromolecular chemistry and physics will need to be extended before we can interpret the transport behavior of biological membranes. Complexities as severe as those encountered in the area of muscle contraction may be met here also.

In pointing to the more direct approaches that may eventually help to bring us to a molecular interpretation of transport, I do not mean to say that the indirect approaches still mainly being pursued have reached a level of diminishing returns. They have given us most of the present conceptions of transport, and they may point out even more closely where the direct attack is to be made.

# *Appendix 1:*
# *Terminological*
# *considerations*

## The term *transport*

With the present enormously increased biological interest in transport we see this term occasionally used very broadly. Without any desire to set arbitrary limits to the biological area interesting to those who work in this field, I urge that we continue to define transport as the process by which a solute is transferred from one phase to another, being in the same initial and final states in the two phases. Let me set up a series of hypothetical examples of the uptake of solutes by tissues or cells, to see how this definition operates:

Case 1. Cupric ion is fixed by liver slices, whether at 37 or 100°, by complexing with accessible groups. Dissociation from superficial sites, followed by more stable association with deeper ones, will be involved.

Case 2. A solute supplied exogenously does not mix with its supposed endogenous equivalent, because the endogenous equivalent is actually a different chemical species. A genetic variant permits mixing, because it has the capacity to convert the solute to the form present endogenously.

Case 3. A tissue (let us assume) incorporates an amino acid into protein at the plasma membrane. Eventually, part of this amino acid appears free (we shall suppose) at a high level in the cells by intracellular proteolysis, perhaps with an average delay of several days.

Case 4. Succinate reacts with an enzyme in the plasma membrane, and the succinyl group is then donated to a series of successive acceptors, some of which are potentially able to yield free succinate ion at a higher level than it exists in the extracellular phase. Let us assume that, in actuality, only very low levels of free succinate are realized, and that the interest is placed in the transfer of the succinyl group.

Case 5. Inorganic phosphate enters a given cell, we shall suppose, by forming ATP and, successively, one or two other phosphoryl compounds, appearing seconds later as inorganic phosphate perhaps at a substantially higher level than that present in the external medium.

Case 6. Glucose enters the red blood cell at a rate so fast as to be measurable only with difficulty. So small an amount of an intermediate exists at any instant that it has defied detection up to the present time. Nevertheless, indirect evidence shows that an intermediate must be formed in the process.

These examples range in nature from the first two cases, which as arbitrarily set forth obviously are not transports, to the last two, which almost everyone will accept as falling within the meaning of the term. By creating the concept of *functional compartmentalization,* Case 2 can be brought rather artificially within the scope of our subject; but surely no merit can be ascribed to calling this a *functional transport.*

In between these extremes we have more or less hypothetical examples that do not meet the above definition for one reason or another. In the third case, the factor of time lag makes it rather absurd to think of the interrupted sequence as a transport.

In Case 4 the interest is in the transfer of a chemical group and not of a molecular species. This process is known as a *group translocation.* The means by which groups are transferred vectorially in this process, as well as from donor to receptor, will undoubtedly receive companion interest to transport and may yet prove to be intrinsic to that subject as the means by which the decisive vectorial step may occur in transport.

The fifth case we can classify as a transport, provided, of course, that we are considering the process as a whole, as a mode of inorganic phosphate entry into the cell. In this transport a phosphoryl translocation, for example as visualized in Figure 17, may prove to be the decisive step, although only a step. The fact that we may know the intermediates in this hypothetical case naturally does not move the case out of the area of transport.

## The term *active transport*

At one time an effort was made to reserve the term *transport* for movements against concentration gradients, the term *transfer* being suitable for movements in any direction (cf. Maizels, 1954). Obviously, this distinction has now been lost. One can only deplore any tendency now to empty of meaning the qualifying adjective in the term *active transport*.

The only generally accepted criterion is that the transport be able to operate against a concentration gradient (Rosenberg, 1954), or that the flux ratio depart from the concentration ratio between the two phases (Ussing, 1949).

Perhaps the adjective *active* has seemed to give a superior standing to a transport so that the temptation to use it without meeting either form of this criterion has been great. The demonstration of a high temperature coefficient is not adequate, nor is a dependence on energy-yielding metabolism convincing, since a steady supply of metabolic energy may serve only to maintain the supply of a transporting or a binding structure. As a further caution, note that dinitrophenol accelerates a mediated entrance of glucose into muscle, but inhibits its uphill transport into kidney slices. Furthermore, one can expect for many solutes that they may be bound to cellular components, so that a demonstration that a cell *accumulates* a given substance does not prove that an active transport (or indeed any transport) has taken place.

## The term *permease*

In 1957 Cohen and Monod wrote:

Thus the role of permeases as chemical connecting links between the external world and the intracellular metabolic world appears to be decisive. . . . Moreover, since the pattern of intermediary metabolism appears more and more to be fundamentally similar in all cells, the characteristic, differential, chemical properties of different cells should depend largely on their permeases.

These chemical connecting links to the outside world are surely the same ones which Höber described early in this century as "the physiological import and export" of the cell (1911). In the absence of a unique demonstration of their makeup and operation, we should be reluctant to accept at this point a new name for the transport processes of all cells, if this was intended, and even more reluctant to accept a unique term for bacterial transport processes in the absence of a sharp differentiation of their nature and function.

The probable relationship of transport to enzyme action has long been recognized. Danielli wrote this summary statement in 1954: "The general conclusion which emerges from these studies is that enzyme-like membrane components appear to be active both in facilitated diffusion and active transport." At the same time he urged reserve in treating the enzymatic aspects as perhaps only incidental to the permeation process. In summarizing studies extending back to 1922, Wilbrandt wrote in the same year (1954), "The assumption that enzymatic reactions are somehow involved in active transport . . . has rather generally been made and in fact can hardly be doubted." Nevertheless, these and many other investigators refrained from giving the enzyme or the enzymatic process a name. The Commission on Enzymes of the International Union of Biochemistry (1961) has ruled that a term containing the -ase suffix should be adopted only for a single enzyme catalyzing a known reaction. This renders official an already widely felt restraint.

If the new term should indeed prove generally acceptable to the whole transport field, the main difficulty of having the term used as if it represented processes peculiar to microorganisms will be avoided.

# Appendix 2:
# Reprint

This essay is reprinted from the *Bulletin of the New England Medical Center* **10,** 108 (1948), as a supplement to the discussion of Chapter 8.

# The Distribution Of Amino Acids
## Between Cellular And Extracellular Fluids
### Relation To Growth

HALVOR N. CHRISTENSEN, Ph. D.

*Director, Department of Research Chemistry, Children's Hospital*

One of the most significant reactions of living matter we can write, light-heartedly, in this way:

$$\text{amino acids} \underset{2}{\overset{1}{\rightleftarrows}} \text{proteins}$$

The balance between reactions 1 and 2 determines whether growth or wasting occurs. All factors that accelerate growth or that accelerate catabolism must affect this balance, possibly by direct effects upon these reactions.

Our approach to the problem has been to break down this reaction into two stages, like this:

$$\left.\begin{array}{l} \text{extracellular} \overset{3}{\underset{4}{\longrightarrow}} \\ \text{amino acids} \longleftarrow \end{array}\right\} \begin{array}{l} \text{cellular} \qquad 1 \\ \text{amino acids} \rightleftarrows \text{proteins} \\ \text{5 to 40 x as} \quad 2 \\ \text{concentrated} \\ \longleftarrow \text{cell boundary} \longrightarrow \end{array}$$

Van Slyke and Meyer pointed out in 1913 that the free amino acids of tissues are at much higher concentration than those of the plasma, and that amino acids enter the tissues against these concentration gradients. The necessary implication of this finding is that each amino acid molecule is brought into the cell by an active, energy-requiring process, undoubtedly enzymatic. Could this be a site of control of protein synthesis and hence of growth? Might testosterone, for example, increase the degree to which muscle cells concentrate amino acids?

First, we have analyzed plasma and tissues to determine if

(*Bulletin of the New England Medical Center X: 108-111, June, 1948*) various types of tissue cells tend to concentrate amino acids to a characteristic extent. By specific ninhydrin procedures, tissue and plasma filtrates were analyzed for glutamine, for glycine, and for the sum of other amino acids, which will be called the "residual" amino acids. Upon the basis of chloride and water analyses, we were able to calculate the concentration of each of these three in the cell water, and the *distribution ratio* between the cellular and extracellular water. Glycine was a fortunate choice; for some reason the glycine of the plasma and tissue of the guinea pig is extremely variable. But the variations in plasma, liver, and muscle *occur together* so that fairly constant distribution ratios are maintained. The liver cell concentration tends to be thirty-three times, and the muscle cell concentration, nine times, that of the extracellular fluid. The residual amino acids tend to be fifteen times as concentrated in the liver cells, five times as concentrated in the muscle cells. Most of the amino acids fed to guinea pigs were metabolized quickly and had small effects upon amino acid distribution. But certain ones were disposed of much more slowly and produced high plasma and tissue concentrations. L-proline, L-histidine, L-methionine and most of the DL-amino acids examined are included. The ability of the cells to concentrate glycine was strikingly reduced when such amino acids were fed. The higher the plasma concentration, the more severe the effect. Similarly, high glycine concentrations interfered with the ability of the tissue cells to concentrate nonglycine amino acids.

Here, we believe, competitive inhibition is occurring among the amino acids. Biologic antagonisms have been recognized between metabolites and their foreign analogues, or even between two analogous compounds both of which are supposedly foreign to the organism, but here is antagonism among a group of essential metabolites. The observations indicate that the concentrating function does not operate independently for each amino acid. A single mechanism could scarcely concentrate every one of the many amino acids and yet maintain steady cell concentrations in the face of the variations of the amino acid mixtures presented.

Protein synthesis obviously requires the presence at some limiting concentration of every amino acid, essential or nonessential, that must go into the protein molecule. When a strongly asymmetric accumulation of amino acids results from feeding or injection, the ability of the cells to retain other amino acids will be handicapped and inhibition of growth or nitrogen retention may be expected. Severe growth inhibition has been observed in diets containing gelatin supplemented with essential amino acids, and in diets containing abnormal amounts of glycine, proline, methionine and other amino acids. If a person is fed glycine it will be found that his plasma alanine goes up; if fed alanine, his plasma glycine rises.

Such an agent as sulfadiazine can be given to a patient according to a variety of dosage schedules. But if his nitrogen nutrition is to be helped, he cannot be given a midday meal that is deficient in methionine and then be given five grams of methionine at two o'clock without doing him anything but harm. Nor can he be given twenty grams of methionine, even with his lunch, on the theory that if a little is good a lot is better.

This question of imbalance is undoubtedly a great deal more delicate when the amino acids are injected intravenously, so that intense changes can be produced quickly in the medium bathing the cell.

Feeding glutamic acid actually reduced the plasma amino acids, both in the guinea pig and in the dog. Tissue analyses indicated that this amino acid increases the extent to which cells concentrate amino acids. This is a clue to the nature of the concentrating process.

Now if growth were accelerated by shifting the equilibrium to the right for reactions 1 and 2, the cellular amino acids should be decreased. A good example is the precipitous fall in the glycine of liver that is produced by its conjugation to form hippuric acid when stimulated by the feeding of sodium benzoate. In two instances of very rapid growth we have observed, instead, elevated amino acids.

Fetal muscle cells of the guinea pig show concentrations of both glycine and residual amino acids three times as high as the maternal muscle cells. Similar relations were observed in the rabbit for both skeletal and cardiac muscle. There are two factors acting to produce these higher concentrations:

1. The placenta concentrates amino acids. This undoubtedly has a large effect on the partitioning of amino acids between the fetus and the mother.

2. The fetal muscle, despite its very rapid growth, concentrates amino acids to a greater extent than does the maternal muscle.

The concentrating activity of the placenta for amino acids

shows much the same characteristics shown by liver or muscle cells:

1.  After glycine was fed it appeared at higher concentrations in the fetal than in the maternal plasma.

2.  When enough L-proline, L-histidine or DL-methionine was fed to produce high plasma levels, the difference between the glycine in the fetal and maternal plasmas was largely abolished.  (Again competition between amino acids is shown.)

3.  L-glutamic acid feeding produced extremely high fetal plasma concentrations without affecting the glycine distribution.

Human fetal plasma showed 1.7 to 1.8 times as high concentrations of glycine and residual amino acids as the maternal plasma, whether obtained at normal deliveries or deliveries by cesarian section.  We are indebted to Dr. Clement Smith and his colleagues for these samples.

A second instance where elevated amino acid concentrations were associated with very rapid growth was during hepatic regeneration after surgical removal of two-thirds of the liver of the rat.  As is known, restoration is very rapid, with mitosis beginning about twenty-four hours after the operation, and the liver remnant doubling its weight during the second and third day.  In coincidence with this growth, after a twenty to twenty-six hour latency the residual amino acids of the liver rose about 50 per cent with an accompanying increase in glutathione. The concentrations and growth rate then subsided together.

Our observations upon fetal muscle and upon regenerating liver support the view that growth acceleration may occur by effects upon the equilibrium reaction 3 and 4 rather than by direct effects upon reactions 1 or 2.  We are extending these observations to other instances of rapid growth.  Probably we are dealing here with two questions:

1.  Is growth a mass action effect resulting when the various amino acids are at adequate concentrations in the cell?

2.  Are changes in the quantitative relation between protein synthesis and catabolism produced by changes in the extent to which the cells concerned concentrate amino acids?  The first question concerns the nature of growth, the second the control of growth.

# References

Ackerman, D., and Kutscher, F. (1911), *Z. Biol.*, **57**, 355.

Agar, W. T., Hird, F. J. R., and Sidhu, G. S. (1953), *J. Physiol. (London)*, **121**, 255.

Agar, W. T., Hird, F. J. R., and Sidhu, G. S. (1956), *Biochim. et Biophys. Acta*, **22**, 21.

Ahmed, K., and Judah, J. D. (1962), *Biochim. et Biophys. Acta*, **57**, 245.

Akedo, H., and Christensen, H. N. (1962a), *J. Biol. Chem.*, **237**, 113.

Akedo, H., and Christensen, H. N. (1962b), *J. Biol. Chem.*, **237**, 118.

Akedo, H., Sugawa, T., Yoshikawa, S., and Suda, M. (1960), *J. Biochem. (Tokyo)*, **47**, 124.

Allfrey, V. G., Meudt, R., Hopkins, J. W., and Mirsky, A. E. (1961), *Proc. Natl. Acad. Sci. U.S.*, **47**, 907.

Alvarado, F., and Crane, R. K. (1962), *Biochim. et Biophys. Acta*, **56**, 170.

Andersson-Cedergren, E. (1959), *J. Ultrastruct. Res.*, **Suppl. 1**, 1.

Barrett, J. T., Larson, A. D., and Kallio, R. E. (1953), *J. Bacteriol.*, **65**, 187.

Barrnett, R. J., and Ball, E. G. (1960), *J. Biophys. Biochem. Cytol.*, **8**, 83.

Battaglia, F. C., and Randle, P. J. (1960), *Biochem. J.*, **75**, 408.

Bennett, H. S. (1956), *J. Biophys. Biochem. Cytol.*, **Suppl.**, 99.

Bergen, S. S., Jr., Sullivan, R., Hilton, J. G., Willis, S. W., Jr., and Van Itallie, T. B. (1960), *Am. J. Physiol.*, **199**, 136.

Brodsky, W. A., Rehm, W. S., and McIntosh, B. J. (1953), *J. Clin. Invest.*, **32**, 556.

Caldwell, P. C. (1959), in J. Coursaget (ed.), *The Method of Isotopic Tracers Applied to the Study of Active Ion Transport*, Pergamon, New York, p. 88.

Caldwell, P. C. (1960), *Arch. Ges. Physiol.*, **272**, 215.

Caldwell, P. C., Hodgkin, A. L., Keynes, R. D., and Shaw, T. I. (1960), *J. Physiol. (London)*, **152**, 561, 591.

Cadenas, E., Kaji, H., Park, C. R., and Rasmussen, H. (1961), *J. Biol. Chem.*, **236**, PC 63.

Christensen, H. N. (1948), *Bull. New England Med. Center*, **10**, 108.

Christensen, H. N. (1955), in W. E. McElroy and B. Glass (eds.), *Amino Acid Metabolism*, Johns Hopkins Press, Baltimore, p. 63.

Christensen, H. N. (1960a), in G. E. W. Wolstenholme and M. O'Connor (eds.), *Metabolic Effects of Adrenal Hormones;* Ciba Foundation Study Group **No. 6,** Churchill, London, p. 56.

Christensen, H. N. (1960b), *Adv. in Prot. Chem.*, **15**, 239.

Christensen, H. N. (1961), in A. Kleinzeller and A. Kotyk (eds.), *Membrane Transport and Metabolism*, Publishing House of the Czechoslovak Academy of Sciences, Prague, p. 470.

Christensen, H. N., and Jones, J. C. (1961), *J. Biol. Chem.*, **236**, 76.

Christensen, H. N., and Jones, J. C. (1962), *J. Biol. Chem.*, **237**, 1203.

Christensen, H. N., and Riggs, T. R. (1952), *J. Biol. Chem.*, **194**, 57.

Christensen, H. N., Akedo, H., Oxender, D. L., and Winter, C. G. (1962), in J. F. Holden (ed.), *Conference on Free Amino Acids*, Elsevier, Amsterdam.

Christensen, H. N., Parker, H. M., and Riggs, T. R. (1958), *J. Biol. Chem.*, **233**, 1485.

Christensen, H. N., Riggs, T. R., and Coyne, B. A. (1954), *J. Biol. Chem.*, **209**, 413.

Christensen, H. N., Riggs, T. R., Fischer, H., and Palatine, I. M. (1952a), *J. Biol. Chem.*, **198**, 1.

Christensen, H. N., Riggs, T. R., Fischer, H., and Palatine, I. M. (1952b), *J. Biol. Chem.*, **198**, 17.

Christensen, H. N., Rothwell, J. T., Sears, R. A., and Streicher, J. A. (1948), *J. Biol. Chem.*, **175**, 101.

Christensen, H. N., Thompson, D. H., Markel, S., and Sidky, M. (1958), *Proc. Soc. Exptl. Biol. Med.*, **99**, 780.

Cirillo, V. P. (1961), *Ann. Rev. Microbiol.*, **15**, 197.

Cohen, G. N., and Monod, J. (1957), *Bacteriol. Rev.*, **21**, 169.

Cohen, G. N., and Rickenberg, H. V. (1955), *Compt. rend.*, **240**, 466.

Cohn, W. E., and Cohn, E. T. (1939), *Proc. Soc. Exptl. Biol. Med.*, **41**, 445.

Collander, R. (1937), *Trans. Faraday Soc.*, **33**, 985.

Conway, E. J., and Duggan, F. (1958), *Biochem. J.*, **69**, 265.

Conway, E. J., and McCormack, J. I. (1953), *J. Physiol. (London)*, **120**, 1.

Crane, R. K. (1960), *Physiol. Revs.*, **40**, 789.

Crane, R. K., and Krane, S. M. (1956), *Biochim. et Biophys. Acta*, **20**, 568.

Crane, R. K., and Mandelstam, P. (1960), *Biochim. et Biophys. Acta*, **45**, 460.

Crane, R. K., Miller, D., and Bihler, I. (1961), in A. Kleinzeller and A. Kotyk (eds.), *Membrane Transport and Metabolism*, Publishing House of the Czechoslovak Academy of Sciences, Prague, p. 439.

Csáky, T. Z. (1938), *Ber. Ges. Biol.*, **108**, 670.

Csáky, T. Z. (1942), *Z. Physiol. Chem.*, **277**, 47.

Csáky, T. Z. (1961), *Am. J. Physiol.*, **201**, 999.

Csáky, T. Z., and Thale, M. (1960), *J. Physiol. (London)*, **151**, 59.

Csáky, T. Z., Hartzog, H. G., and Fernald, G. W. (1961), *Am. J. Physiol.*, **200**, 459.

Danielli, J. F. (1954), in *Proc. Symposium Colston Research Soc.*, **7**, 1.

Danowski, T. S. (1941), *J. Biol. Chem.*, **139**, 693.

Davson, H., and Danielli, J. F. (1943), *The Permeability of Natural Membranes*, Cambridge University Press, Cambridge, pp. 53–57.

Dent, C. E. (1949), *Biochem. Soc. Symp. (Cambridge, Engl.)*, **No. 3**, p. 34.

Dent, C. E., and Rose, G. A. (1951), *Quart. J. Med.*, **20**, 205.

Dent, C. E., Senior, B., and Walshe, J. M. (1954), *J. Clin. Invest.*, **33**, 1216.

Doudoroff, M. (1951), in W. D. McElroy and B. Glass (eds.), *Symposium on Phosphorus Metabolism*, Vol. 1, Johns Hopkins Press, Baltimore, p. 42.

Dunham, E. T. (1957), *Federation Proc.*, **16**, 33.

Dunham, E. T., and Glynn, I. M. (1960), *J. Physiol. (London)*, **152**, 61P.

Ege, R., Gottlieb, E., and Rakestraw, N. W. (1925), *Am. J. Physiol.*, **72**, 76.

Eichhorn, J., Halkerston, I. D. K., Feinstein, M., and Hechter, O. (1960), *Proc. Soc. Exptl. Biol. Med.*, **103**, 515.

Eichhorn, J., and Hechter, O. (1961), *J. Gen. Physiol.*, **45**, 15.

Eisenman, G. (1961), in A. Kleinzeller and A. Kotyk (eds.), *Membrane Transport and Metabolism*, Publishing House of the Czechoslovak Academy of Sciences, Prague, p. 163.

Evans, J. V. (1954), *Nature*, **174**, 931.

Evans, J. V., and King, J. W. B. (1955), *Nature*, **176**, 171.

Faust, R. G. (1960), *J. Cellular Comp. Physiol.*, **56**, 103.

Finch, L. R., and Hird, F. J. R. (1960), *Biochim. et Biophys. Acta*, **43**, 268, 278.

Fischer, A. (1897), *Vorlesungen über Bakterien;* English translation by A. C. Jones, *Structure and Function of Bacteria*, Clarendon Press, Oxford, 1900.

Fischer, A. (1900), *Z. Hygiene*, **35**, 1.

Fisher, R. B., and Lindsay, D. B. (1956), *J. Physiol. (London)*, **131**, 526.

Fong, C. T. O., Silver, L., Christman, D. R., and Schwartz, I. L. (1960), *Proc. Natl. Acad. Sci. U.S.*, **46**, 1273.

Fong, C. T. O., Silver, L., Popenoe, E. A., and Debons, A. F. (1962), *Biochim. et Biophys. Acta*, **56**, 190.

Frazier, H. S., Dempsey, E. F., and Leaf, A. (1962), *J. Gen. Physiol.*, **45**, 529.

Gale, E. F. (1953), *Adv. in Prot. Chem.*, **8**, 285.

Gale, E. F., and Van Halteren, M. B. (1952), *Biochem. J.*, **50**, 34.

Gardos, G. (1954), *Acta Physiol. Acad. Sci. Hung.*, **6**, 191.

Gilby, A. R., and Few, A. V. (1958), *Biochim. et Biophys. Acta*, **30**, 421.

Glynn, I. M. (1957a), *Progr. Biophys. Biophys. Chem.*, **8**, 241.

Glynn, I. M. (1957b), *J. Physiol. (London)*, **136**, 148.

Goldacre, R. J. (1952), *Intern. Rev. Cytol.*, **1**, 135.

Harris, J. E. (1940), *Biol. Bull.*, **79**, 373.

Harris, J. E. (1941), *J. Biol. Chem.*, **141**, 579.

Harvey, E. N. (1943), in H. Davson and J. F. Danielli, *The Permeability of Natural Membranes*, Cambridge University Press, Cambridge, Foreword.

Hechter, O., and Lester, G. (1960), *Recent Progr. Hormone Res.*, **16**, 139.

Heinz, E. (1954), *J. Biol. Chem.*, **211**, 781.

Heinz, E., and Patlak, C. S. (1960), *Biochim. et Biophys. Acta*, **44**, 324.

Heinz, E., and Walsh, P. M. (1958), *J. Biol. Chem.*, **233**, 1488.

Hempling, H. G., and Hare, D. (1961), *J. Biol. Chem.*, **236**, 2498.

Herzenberg, L. A. (1961), *Arch. Biochem. Biophys.*, **93**, 314.

Hillier, J., and Hoffman, J. F. (1953), *J. Cellular Comp. Physiol.*, **42**, 203.

Hilton, J. G., Scian, L. F., Westermann, C. D., and Kruesi, O. R. (1959), *Science*, **129**, 971.

Hoagland, M. B., Zamecnik, P. C., Sharon, N., Lipmann, F., Stulberg, M. P., and Boyer, P. D. (1957), *Biochim. et Biophys. Acta*, **26**, 215.

Höber, R. (1902), *Physikalische Chemie der Zelle und Gewebe*, Engelmann, Leipzig.

Höber, R. (1911), *Physikalische Chemie der Zelle und Gewebe,* 3rd ed., Engelmann, Leipzig.

Höber, R. (1914), *Biochem. Z.,* **60,** 253 (in Kozawa, S., *ibid.,* p. 231).

Hoffman, J. F. (1958), *J. Gen. Physiol.,* **42,** 9.

Hokin, L. E., and Hokin, M. R. (1958), *J. Biol. Chem.,* **233,** 805, 818.

Hokin, L. E., and Hokin, M. R. (1959a), *J. Biol. Chem.,* **234,** 1387.

Hokin, L. E., and Hokin, M. R. (1959b), *Nature,* **184,** 1068.

Hokin, L. E., and Hokin, M. R. (1962), *Federation Proc.,* to be published; oral communication.

Holter, H. (1959), *Intern. Rev. Cytol.,* **8,** 481.

Horecker, B. L., Osborn, M. J., McLellan, W. L., Avigad, G., and Asensio, C. (1961), in A. Kleinzeller and A. Kotyk (eds.), *Membrane Transport and Metabolism,* Publishing House of the Czechoslovak Academy of Sciences, Prague, p. 378.

Horecker, B. L., Thomas, J., and Monod, J. (1960), *J. Biol. Chem.,* **235,** 1586.

International Union of Biochemistry (1961), Symp. Ser. 20, Report of the Commission on Enzymes, Pergamon, Oxford, p. 29.

Jacobs, F. A., and Hillman, R. S. L. (1958), *J. Biol. Chem.,* **232,** 445.

Jacobs, F. A., Coen, L J., and Hillman, R. S. L. (1960), *J. Biol. Chem.,* **235,** 1372.

Jacques, J. A. (1961), *Proc. Natl. Acad. Sci. U.S.,* **47,** 153.

Jacquez, J. A. (1961), *Am. J. Physiol.,* **200,** 1063.

Järnefelt, J. (1961), *Biochem. Biophys. Res. Commun.,* **6,** 285.

Jorgensen, C. R., Landau, B. R., and Wilson, T. H. (1961), *Am. J. Physiol.,* **200,** 111.

Kalman, S. M., and Lombrozo, M. E. (1961), *J. Pharmacol. Exptl. Therap.,* **131,** 265.

Kalman, S. M., Lombrozo, M. E., and Lavis, V. (1961), *Science,* **134,** 1372.

Kaplan, S. A., and Nagareda, C. S. (1961), *Am. J. Physiol.,* **200,** 1035.

Karnovsky, M. L., and Sbarra, A. J. (1960), *Am. J. Clin. Nutr.,* **8,** 147.

Kepes, A. (1960), *Biochim. et Biophys. Acta,* **40,** 70.

Kernan, R. P. (1961), *Nature,* **190,** 347.

Kerr, S. E. (1937), *J. Biol. Chem.,* **117,** 227.

Keston, A. S. (1954), *Science,* **120,** 355.

Kipnis, D. M., and Cori, C. F. (1957), *J. Biol. Chem.,* **224,** 681.

Kipnis, D. M., and Cori, C. F. (1959), *J. Biol. Chem.,* **234,** 171.

Kipnis, D. M., and Noall, M. W. (1958), *Biochim. et Biophys. Acta,* **28,** 226.

Kleinzeller, A., and Kotyk, A. (1961), *Biochim. et Biophys. Acta,* **54,** 367.

Koefoed-Johnsen, V., and Ussing, H. H. (1953), *Acta Physiol. Scand.*, **28,** 60.

Kogut, M., and Podoski, E. P. (1953), *Biochem. J.*, **55,** 800.

Kostyo, J. L., and Engel, F. L. (1960), *Endocrinol.*, **67,** 708.

Kostyo, J. L., Hotchkiss, J., and Knobil, E. (1959), *Science,* **130,** 1653.

Krane, S. M., and Crane, R. K. (1959), *J. Biol. Chem.*, **234,** 211.

Lassen, U. V. (1961), *Biochim. et Biophys. Acta,* **53,** 557.

Leach, F. R., and Snell, E. E. (1959), *Biochim. et Biophys. Acta,* **34,** 292.

Leach, F. R., and Snell, E. E. (1960), *J. Biol. Chem.*, **235,** 3523.

LeFevre, P. G. (1961a), *Pharmacol. Revs.*, **13,** 39.

LeFevre, P. G. (1961b), *Federation Proc.*, **20,** 139.

LeFevre, P. G. (1961c), *Nature,* **191,** 970.

LeFevre, P. G., and Marshall, J. K. (1958), *Am. J. Physiol.*, **194,** 333.

LeFevre, P. G., and Marshall, J. K. (1959), *J. Biol. Chem.*, **234,** 3022.

LeFevre, P. G., and McGinnis, G. F. (1960), *J. Gen. Physiol.*, **44,** 87.

Lehninger, A. L. (1959), *J. Biol. Chem.*, **234,** 2187.

Lehninger, A. L. (1960a), *Ann. N.Y. Acad. Sci.*, **86,** 484.

Lehninger, A. L. (1960b), in T. W. Goodwin (ed.), *Biological Structure and Function,* Academic, New York, in press.

Lehninger, A. L., and Neubert, D. (1961), *Proc. Natl. Acad. Sci. U.S.,* **47,** 1929.

Lehninger, A. L., Wadkins, C. L., Cooper, C., Devlin, T. M., and Gamble, J. L., Jr. (1958), *Science,* **128,** 450.

Levine, R. (1961), *Diabetes,* **10,** 421.

Levine, R., Goldstein, M. S., Klein, S., and Huddlestun, B. (1949), *J. Biol. Chem.*, **179,** 985.

Lewis, W. H. (1931), *Bull. Johns Hopkins Hosp.*, **49,** 17.

Lundegaardh, H. (1939), *Nature,* **143,** 203.

Lundsgaard, E. (1939), *Acta Soc. Med. Upsalien.*, **45,** 143.

Luzzatto, L., and Leoncini, G. (1961), *Ital. Biochem. J.* (Eng. edition, *Giorn. Biochim.*), **10,** 249.

Maizels, M. (1954), *Symp. Soc. Exptl. Biol.*, **8,** 211.

Manchester, K. L. (1961), *Biochem. J.*, **81,** 135.

Manchester, K. L., and Young, F. G. (1960), *Biochem. J.*, **75,** 487.

Manery, J. F. (1954), *Physiol. Revs.*, **34,** 334.

Manery, J. F., Gourley, D. R. H., and Fisher, K. C. (1956), *Can. J. Biochem. Physiol.*, **34,** 893.

Marquis, R. E. (1961), Ph.D. Thesis, The University of Michigan (with P. Gerhardt).

Masing, E. (1914), *Arch. Ges. Physiol.*, **156,** 401.

Melhuish, A. H., and Greenbaum, A. L. (1961), *Biochem. J.*, **78**, 392.

Mitchell, P. (1960a), in A. Kleinzeller and A. Kotyk (eds.), *Membrane Transport and Metabolism*, Publishing House of the Czechoslovak Academy of Sciences, Prague, p. 22.

Mitchell, P. (1960b), in T. W. Goodwin (ed.), *Biological Structure and Function*, Academic, New York, in press; cited by Mitchell (1961).

Mitchell, P. (1961a), *Biochem. J.*, **79**, 23P.

Mitchell, P. (1961b), *Nature*, **191**, 144.

Mitchell, P. (1961c), *Biochem. J.*, **81**, 24P.

Mitchell, P., and Moyle, J. (1956), *Symp. Soc. Gen. Microbiol.*, **6**, 150.

Mitchell, P., and Moyle, J. (1958a), *Nature*, **182**, 372.

Mitchell, P., and Moyle, J. (1958b), *Proc. Roy. Phys. Soc. Edinburgh*, **27**, 61.

Monod, J. (1956), in O. H. Gaebler (ed.), *Enzymes, Units of Biological Structure and Function*, Academic, New York, p. 7.

Mora, J. (1961), personal communication.

Mueller, P., Rudin, D. O., Ti Tien, H., and Wescott, W. C. (1962), *Nature*, **194**, 979.

Myers, D. K., and Slater, E. C. (1957), *Biochem. J.*, **67**, 558.

Neubert, D., and Lehninger, A. L. (1962), *J. Biol. Chem.*, **237**, 952.

Newey, H., and Smyth, D. H. (1959a), *J. Physiol.*, **145**, 48.

Newey, H., and Smyth, D. H. (1959b), *J. Physiol.*, **146**, 11P.

Noall, M. W., and Allen, W. M. (1961), *J. Biol. Chem.*, **236**, 2987.

Noall, M. W., Riggs, T. R., Walker, L. M., and Christensen, H. N. (1957), *Science*, **126**, 1002.

Orloff, J., Handler, J. S., and Preston, A. S. (1962), *J. Clin. Invest.*, **41**, 702.

Ørskov, S. L. (1935), *Biochem. Z.*, **279**, 241.

Osterhout, W. J. V. (1933), *Ergeb. Physiol., Biol. Chem. Exptl. Pharmakol.*, **35**, 967; in English.

Overgaard-Hansen, K., and Lassen, U. V. (1959), *Nature*, **184**, 553.

Overton, E. (1899), *Vierteljahresschr. Naturforsch. Ges. Zürich Beih.*, **44**, 88.

Overton, E. (1902), *Arch. Ges. Physiol.*, **92**, 115.

Oxender, D. L. (1962a), *Federation Proc.*, **21**, 148.

Oxender, D. L. (1962b), unpublished results.

Oxender, D. L., and Christensen, H. N. (1959), *J. Biol. Chem.*, **234**, 2321.

Pal, P. R., and Christensen, H. N. (1959), *J. Biol. Chem.*, **234**, 613.

Pal, P. R., and Christensen, H. N. (1961), *J. Biol. Chem.*, **236**, 894.

Palade, G. E. (1956), *J. Biophys. Biochem. Cytol.*, **2**, Suppl., 85.

Palade, G. E. (1961), *Circulation*, **24**, 371.

Park, C. R., Post, R. L., Kalman, C. F., Wright, J. H., Jr., Johnson, L. H., and Morgan, H. E. (1956), *Ciba Found. Colloq. Endocrinol.*, **9**, 257.

Patlak, C. S. (1957), *Bull. Math. Biol.*, **19**, 209.

Peters, R. A. (1956), *Nature*, **177**, 426.

Pittman, J. A., Boshell, B. R., Williams, B. H., Hamner, D., and Hill, P. (1961), *Biochem. Biophys. Res. Commun.*, **6**, 29.

Pletscher, A., von Planta, P., and Hunzinger, W. A. (1955), *Helv. Physiol. Pharmacol. Acta*, **13**, 18.

Ponder, E. (1948), *Hemolysis and Related Phenomena*, Grune & Stratton, New York.

Post, R. L. (1959), *Federation Proc.*, **18**, 121.

Post, R. L., Merritt, C. R., Kinsolving, C. R., and Albright, C. D. (1960), *J. Biol. Chem.*, **235**, 1796.

Raaflaub, J. (1953), *Helv. Physiol. Pharmacol. Acta*, **11**, 142, 157.

Randle, P. J. (1956), *Nature*, **178**, 983.

Randle, P. J., and Smith, G. H. (1958), *Biochem. J.*, **70**, 490, 501.

Rapoport, S., and Guest, G. M. (1939), *J. Biol. Chem.*, **131**, 675.

Rasmussen, H. (1959), *Endocrinology*, **65**, 517.

Riggs, T. R., and Walker, L. M. (1958), *J. Biol. Chem.*, **233**, 132.

Riggs, T. R., and Walker, L. M. (1960), *J. Biol. Chem.*, **235**, 3603.

Riggs, T. R., and Walker, L. M. (1962), *Federation Proc.*, **21**, 209.

Riggs, T. R., Christensen, H. N., and Palatine, I. M. (1952), *J. Biol. Chem.*, **194**, 53.

Riggs, T. R., Coyne, B. A., and Christensen, H. N. (1954), *J. Biol. Chem.*, **209**, 395.

Riggs, T. R., Walker, L. M., and Christensen, H. N. (1958), *J. Biol. Chem.*, **233**, 1479.

Roberts, R. B., Abelson, P. H., Cowie, D. B., Bolton, E. T., and Britten, R. J. (1957), *Studies of Biosynthesis in Escherichia coli*, Carnegie Inst. Wash. Publ. No. 607.

Robinson, J. R. (1950), *Nature*, **166**, 989.

Robinson, J. R. (1954), *Symp. Soc. Exptl. Biol.*, **8**, 42.

Rosenberg, L. E., Downing, S. J., and Segal, S. (1962), *J. Biol. Chem.*, **237**, 2265.

Rosenberg, T. (1954), *Symp. Soc. Exptl. Biol.*, **8**, 27.

Rosenberg, T. (1961), *Path. Biol.*, **9**, 795.

Rosenberg, T., and Wilbrandt, W. (1957), *J. Gen. Physiol.*, **41**, 289.

Schachter, D., and Rosen, S. M. (1959), *Am. J. Physiol.*, **196**, 357.

Schatzmann, H. J. (1953), *Helv. Physiol. Pharmacol. Acta*, **11**, 346.

Schultz, S. G., and Solomon, A. K. (1961), *J. Gen. Physiol.*, **45**, 355.

Schwartz, I. L., Rasmussen, H., Schoessler, M. A., Fong, C. T. O., and Silver, L. (1960), *J. Clin. Invest.*, **39**, 1026.

Schwartz, I. L., Rasmussen, H., Schoessler, M. A., Silver, L., and Fong, C. T. O. (1960), *Proc. Natl. Acad. Sci. U.S.*, **46**, 1288.

Sen, A. K., and Widdas, W. F. (1962), *J. Physiol. (London)*, **160**, 392, 404.

Shaw, T. I. (1954), Ph.D. Thesis, Cambridge University; cited by I. M. Glynn, in *Progr. Biophys. Biophys. Chem.*, **8**, 241 (1957).

Shaw, T. I. (1959), *Proc. Roy. Soc. (London)*, **B150**, 356.

Shaw, W. V., Lannon, T. J., and Tapley, D. F. (1959), *Biochim. et Biophys. Acta*, **36**, 499.

Sistrom, W. R. (1958), *Biochim. et Biophys. Acta*, **29**, 579.

Sjøstrand, F. S. (1959), in J. L. Oncley (ed.), *Biophysical Science: A Study Program*, Wiley, New York.

Skou, J. C. (1957), *Biochim. et Biophys. Acta*, **23**, 394.

Skou, J. C. (1960), *Biochim. et Biophys. Acta*, **42**, 6.

Skou, J. C. (1961), paper read at *Symposium on Drugs and Membranes at the First International Pharmacological Congress*, Stockholm, August, 1961; manuscript received as a personal communication.

Smillie, L. B., and Manery, J. F. (1960), *Am. J. Physiol.*, **198**, 67.

Solomon, A. K., Gill, T. J., III, and Gold, G. L. (1956), *J. Gen. Physiol.*, **40**, 327.

Stein, W. D. (1956), *Exptl. Cell Research*, **11**, 232.

Stein, W. D. (1958), *Nature*, **181**, 1662.

Stein, W. D. (1961a), *Nature*, **191**, 352.

Stein, W. D. (1961b), *Nature*, **191**, 1277.

Stein, W. D., and Danielli, J. F. (1956), *Discussions Faraday Soc.*, **21**, 238.

Stein, W. H. (1951), *Proc. Soc. Exptl. Biol. Med.*, **78**, 705.

Stone, R. W., and Wilson, P. W. (1952), *J. Bact.*, **63**, 605.

Straub, F. B. (1953), *Acta Physiol. Acad. Sci. Hung.*, **4**, 235.

Székely, M., Manyai, S., and Straub, F. B. (1952), *Acta Physiol. Acad. Sci. Hung.*, **3**, 571.

Szent-Györgyi, A. (1957), *Bioenergetics*, Academic, New York.

Szent-Györgyi, A. (1960), *Introduction to Submolecular Biology*, Academic, New York.

Tapley, D. F. (1956), *J. Biol. Chem.*, **222**, 325.

Tapley, D. F., Cooper, C., and Lehninger, A. L. (1955), *Biochim. et Biophys. Acta*, **18**, 597.

Teorell, T. (1952), *J. Gen. Physiol.*, **35**, 669.

Tosteson, D. C. (1959), *Acta Physiol. Scand.*, **46**, 19.

Tosteson, D. C., Moulton, R. H., and Blaustein, M. (1960), *Federation Proc.*, **19**, 128.

Ueda, K., Akedo, H., and Suda, M. (1960), *J. Biochem. (Tokyo)*, **48**, 584.

Ussing, H. H. (1949), *Physiol. Revs.*, **29**, 127.

Ussing, H. H., and Zerahn, K. (1951), *Acta Physiol. Scand.*, **23**, 110.

Van Slyke, D. D., Wu, H., and McLean, F. C. (1923), *J. Biol. Chem.*, **56**, 765.

Weissbach, H., Redfield, B. G., and Titus, E. (1960), *Nature*, **185**, 99.

Wilbrandt, W. (1954), *Symp. Soc. Exptl. Biol.*, **8**, 136.

Wilbrandt, W. (1956), *J. Cellular Comp. Physiol.*, **47**, 137.

Wilbrandt, W., and Rosenberg, T. (1961), *Pharmacol. Revs.*, **13**, 109.

Wilson, T. H. (1954), *Science*, **120**, 104.

Wilson, T. H., and Crane, R. K. (1958), *Biochim. et Biophys. Acta*, **29**, 30.

Wilson, T. H., and Wiseman, G. (1954), *J. Physiol. (London)*, **123**, 116.

Winter, C. G. (1962), *Federation Proc.*, **21**, 148.

Wiseman, G. (1955), *J. Physiol. (London)*, **127**, 414.

Wolff, J., and Maurey, J. R. (1958), *Nature*, **182**, 957.

Zabin, I., Kepes, A., and Monod, J. (1959), *Biochem. Biophys. Res. Commun.*, **1**, 289.

Zabin, I., Kepes, A., and Monod, J. (1962), *J. Biol. Chem.*, **237**, 253.

Zierler, K. L. (1961), *Bull. Johns Hopkins Hosp.*, **109**, 35.

# Index

Active transport, definition of, 25, 30, 111
Adenosine-3',5'-cyclic phosphate, 98
Adenosine triphosphate
breakdown and transport of, 27, 36, 63, 84–89
electron migrations and, 88–89
introduction of into red cell ghost, 75
linkage to membrane, 87–88
sodium extrusion and, 82–83
sugar transport and, 100
Adrenocorticotrophic hormone, 98, 104
Alanine, 39, 57–59
Aldosterone, 95
Alkali metal distribution
amino acid transport and, 25–26, 79, 83, 86–87
intestinal transport and, 26, 79
sugar transport and, 26, 79
Amebae, 27, 41
Amino acid transport
alanine-preferring, 58–59, 61–62
in bacteria, 59, 65, 92
in Ehrlich cell, 39, 55–65

in erythrocyte, 39, 64
in intestine, 39, 59, 64
in liver, 97, 113, 116
metal transport and, 54, 86–87
optical specificity and, 57–58
in placenta, 115–116
structural specificity and, 37–39, 54–65
tissue slices and, 97
valine-preferring, 57–59, 61–62
1-Aminocyclopentanecarboxylic acid, 56, 65, 90, 96
α-Aminoisobutyric acid, 56–59, 61–64, 90, 96, 103–104
Arginine phosphate, 82–83
ATPase activity and transport, 81
"chemiosmotic" hypothesis and, 84–86
mitochondrial contraction and, 84
in potassium-low erythrocytes, 83

Barrier action, 4, 11, 13–15
Binding, as a basis for accumulation, 111